SOCIETY FOR EXPERIMENTAL BIOLOGY
SEMINAR SERIES · 1

EFFECTS OF AIR POLLUTANTS
ON PLANTS

EFFECTS OF
AIR POLLUTANTS
ON PLANTS

Edited by

T. A. MANSFIELD

Reader in Plant Physiology
University of Lancaster

CAMBRIDGE UNIVERSITY PRESS
CAMBRIDGE
LONDON · NEW YORK · MELBOURNE

Published by the Syndics of the Cambridge University Press
The Pitt Building, Trumpington Street, Cambridge CB2 1RP
Bentley House, 200 Euston Road, London NW1 2DB
32 East 57th Street, New York, NY 10022, USA
296 Beaconsfield Parade, Middle Park, Melbourne 3206, Australia

First published 1976

Printed in Great Britain by
Cox & Wyman Ltd, London, Fakenham and Reading

Library of Congress Cataloguing in Publication Data

Main entry under title:

Effects of air pollutants on plants

(Society for Experimental Biology seminar series; 1)

1. Plants, Effect of air pollution on – Congresses.
I. Mansfield, Terence Arthur. II. Series:
Society for Experimental Biology (Gt. Brit.). Society
for Experimental Biology seminar series ; 1.
QK751.E35   581.5'222   75-32449
ISBN 0 521 21087 9 hard covers
ISBN 0 521 29039 2 paperback

CONTENTS

CONTRIBUTORS

Bell, J. N. B.,
Department of Botany, Imperial College Field Station,
Silwood Park, Sunninghill, Ascot, Berks, UK.

Biscoe, P. V.,
University of Nottingham, School of Agriculture,
Sutton Bonington, Loughborough, Leics, UK.

Black, V.,
University of Nottingham, School of Agriculture,
Sutton Bonington, Loughborough, Leics, UK.

Blakemore, J.,
Department of Plant Biology, University of Newcastle-upon-Tyne,
Newcastle-upon-Tyne NE1 7RU, UK.

Bradshaw, A. D.,
Department of Botany, University of Liverpool,
PO Box 147, Liverpool L69 3BX, UK.

Capron, T. M.,
Department of Biological Sciences, University of Lancaster,
Lancaster LA1 4YQ, UK.

Chan, H.-S.,
Department of Biological Sciences, University of Lancaster,
Lancaster LA1 4YQ, UK.

Davison, A. W.,
Department of Plant Biology, University of Newcastle-upon-Tyne,
Newcastle-upon-Tyne NE1 7RU, UK.

Ernst, W.,
Biological Laboratories, Department of Ecology, Free University,
De Boelelaan 1087, Amsterdam – Buitenveldert, The Netherlands.

Feder, W. A.,
Suburban Experiment Station, University of Massachusetts,
Waltham, Massachusetts 02154, USA.

Horsman, D. C.,
Department of Biological Sciences, University of Lancaster,
Lancaster LA1 4YQ, UK.

McCune, D. C.,
Boyce Thompson Institute,
1086 North Broadway, Yonkers, New York 10701, USA.

MacLean, D. C.,
Boyce Thompson Institute,
1086 North Broadway, Yonkers, New York 10701, USA.

Manning, W. J.,
Suburban Experiment Station, University of Massachusetts,
Waltham, Massachusetts 02154, USA.

Mudd, C. H.,
Agricultural Development and Advisory Service,
Great House Experimental Husbandry Farm,
Helmshore, Rossendale, Lancs, UK.

Nieboer, E.,
Department of Chemistry, Laurentian University,
Sudbury, Ontario, Canada.

Puckett, K. J.,
Department of Biology, Laurentian University,
Sudbury, Ontario, Canada.

Richardson, D. H. S.,
Department of Biology, Laurentian University,
Sudbury, Ontario, Canada.

Rutter, A. J.,
Botany Department, Imperial College,
Prince Consort Road, London SW7 2BB, UK.

Schneider, R. E.,
Boyce Thompson Institute,
1086 North Broadway, Yonkers, New York 10701, USA.

Tomassini, F. D.,
Department of Chemistry, Laurentian University,
Sudbury, Ontario, Canada.

Unsworth, M. H.,
University of Nottingham, School of Agriculture,
Sutton Bonington, Loughborough, Leics, UK.

Wellburn, A. R.,
Department of Biological Sciences, University of Lancaster,
Lancaster LA1 4YQ, UK.

Willix, R.,*
Department of Chemistry, Western Australian Institute of Technology,
Hayman Road, South Bentley 6102, Western Australia.

* The article was written when the author held a Visiting Fellowship at the University of Lancaster.

PREFACE

Studies of the effects of air pollutants on plants have often been criticised because they have over-emphasised the visual symptoms of damage, and have largely consisted of observations made in the field or under unsophisticated experimental conditions. While there is some justification for this criticism, there have also been experimental studies of a more rigorous nature that have led to important advances in our knowledge of the way air pollutants attack metabolic processes, or affect the plant's functioning at the physiological level. It was the purpose of the SEB Seminar held in the University of Liverpool on 10 April 1975 to bring together leading exponents of the experimental approach, and the papers presented covered most of the air pollutants considered to be most damaging to plant life. This volume, based on the seminar, will therefore serve as an introduction to the subject for undergraduates, research students and others, and hopefully will stimulate more scientists to become interested in this important area.

We can foresee that as the subject develops, it will be increasingly necessary for biologists to consider the reactions and interactions between atmospheric pollutants. For this reason the editor invited a physical chemist to prepare an Appendix to this volume to serve as an introduction to a subject that most biologists (and even some chemists) find difficult. Two of the contributors have also prepared an Appendix of tables listing known metabolic and biochemical effects of some of the major air pollutants, and these are intended as guides to the existing literature for those who wish to pursue the responses to particular pollutants in more detail.

The assistance of Dr P. J. W. Saunders in the planning of the meeting was invaluable, and thanks are also due to Dr T. W. Ashenden, Dr R. M. Harrison, Dr T. M. Roberts and Dr A. R. Wellburn for time spent in reading through the typescripts. The Society for Experimental Biology would like to acknowledge, with gratitude, financial assistance from the following sources towards the cost of running the Seminar: Technicon Ltd, Varian Associates Ltd, C. F. Casella & Co. Ltd, T.E.M. Sales Ltd, the British Council, Gelman Hawksley Ltd, the Central Electricity Generating Board, and the Agricultural Research Council.

T. A. Mansfield
Editor for the Society for
Experimental Biology

July, 1975

A.J.RUTTER

Introduction

Shortly before the Seminar one of the contributors asked me whether its object was to review results or identify problems. This field, the investigation of the biological effects of pollution, is one in which there is considerable activity and the Seminar could hardly have been held were it not that many people have results from good experimental work to present. Nevertheless we have a long way to go, for we just do not know, quantitatively, what are the effects – whether great or small – of atmospheric pollution on our wildlife, agriculture and forestry. Before we can answer this question there are many scientific problems to be solved and experimental difficulties to be overcome, and this Seminar was particularly timely in bringing together a large number of scientists to share discussion and information on problems so far encountered.

I should like to begin the volume by outlining some of the problems which I see in the field of atmospheric pollution and its effects on plants. Some of them will be taken up in more detail in later chapters and some fall outside the scope of the book but are nevertheless very relevant to our work. The contributions will no doubt bring to light other problems than those I enumerate.

First of all, pollution is an ecological problem and as such demands an equal understanding of both environment and organisms. Our first need is to measure the environment, and there is still a shortage of satisfactory apparatus for continuously monitoring the low absolute concentrations in which most atmospheric pollutants occur. Where continuous monitoring has been used it has frequently revealed large fluctuations and the occurrence of high concentrations persisting for hours or days, say ten times or more greater than a longer-term mean. This country has an extensive sampling system for sulphur dioxide and smoke but its data are commonly expressed as weekly or monthly means, and much exploratory experimentation has matched treatment concentrations to these mean levels. We are now reaching a stage where more work is needed on the effects of short incidents of high concentration.

Then there is the whole field of transport and circulation of pollutants in the biosphere. Long-range transport and large-scale circulation phenomena are clearly outside the scope of this book, but it has become clear that plants are strong sinks for many gaseous pollutants, that there are marked concentration gradients in the vicinity of vegetation and that, as with so many other environmental factors, the concept of a plant growing in an independently determined concentration is over-simple. Rather there is often rapid absorption, of which local concentration gradients are a reflection. Analyses of the analogous exchanges of carbon dioxide and water vapour between vegetation and atmosphere have considerably assisted our understanding of the absorption of gaseous pollutants, and it is good that the organisers of the Seminar invited two papers on absorption processes. It need hardly be said that the analysis of the environment and its effects needs carefully planned co-operation between biologists and applied physicists and chemists.

Turning now to the effects on plants, there are I think four basic techniques which have been used to investigate the ecological effects of other classes of environmental factors. These are:

(1) Correlation of plant growth and behaviour with variation of the factor in space or time. This has sometimes been used to good effect in relation to pollution but as a general method is subject to the well-known difficulties of identifying causes from field correlations. To this Society, it is unnecessary to stress the value of experiments.

(2) Artificial alteration of the environment, e.g. addition of inorganic nutrients, water, shading, with suitable controls.

(3) Simulation of natural environments in controlled conditions.

(4) Diagnostic physiological analysis of plants in the field; e.g. leaf analysis as an indication of plant nutrient status, determination of leaf water potential as an index of water stress, analysis of root xylem sap for various products of anaerobic respiration in relation to flooding injury or tolerance.

It is clearly very difficult to change the level of pollutants on limited areas and with adequate controls in the outdoor environment and so most experimenters in this field have relied on controlled-environment chambers and cabinets. They mostly experience doubts as to how effectively they can simulate the outdoor environment or extrapolate from their results to field conditions. Do they over-stress the artificiality of the controlled environment or have workers in other fields been too insensitive to this? The answer is probably that conclusions have the most firm basis when they rest on a combination of experiments both in the field and in controlled environment. In a context where field experimentation, i.e. the alteration of pollutant levels, is very difficult, the specification and design of controlled environment clearly needs careful attention. Open-top chambers, with pollutants blown in at the bottom and out through the top, are attractive in that they appear to control the pollution factor with least alteration of the rest of the environment, and their design and use will be discussed in the chapter by McCune *et al.*

We come now to analysing the effects on plants. It would be very useful if, when shown some apparently unhealthy plants in the field, one could perform physiological tests, reasonably specific to particular pollutants and related in the scale of their responses to the growth responses of the plants. I do not decry the search for such tests – I am to some extent engaged in it myself in relation to sulphur dioxide injury – however there is a danger here of allowing pressing practical considerations to persuade us to put the cart before the horse. In general I am sure it is more important to investigate systematically the physiological mechanisms of responses to pollutants, with which many of the following chapters are concerned, and that the more such work is undertaken the sooner we shall be able to assess the effects of specific pollutants in the field.

A move forward from the investigation of single factors is to be welcomed for there is increasing evidence that mixtures of pollutants interact not only chemically in the atmosphere but also physiologically at the plant level.

Finally, pollution is a recent phenomenon in the environment. Plants have been selected by other environmental factors over very long times and evolution has produced morphologically distinct species with fairly well defined tolerances (although often with ecotypic variation). But in response to pollutants we see the early stages of selection operating and in numbers of species there have been found highly resistant genotypes apparently indistinguishable morphologically from normal populations. The final chapter by Bradshaw will discuss this phenomenon.

I began by saying that we do not know the magnitude of the effects of atmospheric pollution, in this or any other country. To make progress we must enlarge our understanding of the environment, maintain a critical attitude to methods of experimentation, press on with investigations of physiological mechanisms of response, and take full account of the genetic variability of our natural vegetation and economic plants.

M.H.UNSWORTH, P.V.BISCOE & V.BLACK

Analysis of gas exchange between plants and polluted atmospheres

Introduction

Exchanges of gases between plants and the atmosphere are essential features of physiological processes such as photosynthesis, respiration and transpiration; the uptake of gaseous pollutants by plants is another example of gas exchange. In discussing the design and analysis of experiments to study effects of air pollutants on gas exchange, we will use examples of effects of sulphur dioxide, but the *principles* apply to any gaseous pollutant.

Studies of effects of sulphur dioxide on plants began late in the nineteenth century and the voluminous literature has been reviewed frequently (e.g. Thomas, 1961; Daines, 1968). In general, research has progressed along two lines. First, responses at the cellular level have been studied, showing for example, disruption of chloroplasts in plants exposed to sulphur dioxide (Wellburn, Majernik & Wellburn, 1972), and changes in activities of enzymes (Pahlich, 1975). This type of work is needed to identify sensitive mechanisms, but it cannot be extrapolated to predict how whole plants will respond to a specific period of exposure to sulphur dioxide at a given concentration. The second and more common line of research is concerned with the response to an atmospheric pollutant of leaves, whole plants and crops, e.g. changes in the rate of photosynthesis (Thomas & Hill, 1937; Sij & Swanson, 1974; Watson, 1974), transpiration (Majernik & Mansfield, 1971; Biscoe, Unsworth & Pinckney, 1973) or of dry matter production (Thomas & Hill, 1937; Bell & Clough, 1973; Bleasdale, 1973). The objective of these studies was to provide information of practical use, e.g. in defining minimum concentrations at which a pollutant is likely to reduce yield, but interpretation of experimental results is complicated because plants respond to many other environmental factors.

One example of a problem of interpretation is the continuing controversy over 'invisible injury' by sulphur dioxide, a term coined to describe effects such as reduction in growth and yield when there are no visible lesions on tissue. After a long series of experiments with various species in the USA, Katz (1949) concluded that yields were not reduced without visible damage, and the 'invisible injury' theory fell into disrepute. However, interest in the topic revived following experiments by Bleasdale (1973) and Bell & Clough (1973) who found that yields of ryegrass growing in chambers containing sulphur dioxide at concentrations insufficient to cause visible injury were much less than yields in identical chambers containing filtered air. In contrast, however, Cowling, Jones & Lockyer (1973) found that yields of ryegrass growing in sulphur-deficient soils were greater when the surrounding air contained low concentrations of sulphur dioxide than when clean air was used. When soils with adequate sulphur were used, yields between 'clean' and 'polluted' chambers did not differ significantly. Physiological effects have also been found at sulphur dioxide concentrations below the visible injury threshold. Majernik & Mansfield (1971) and Biscoe *et al.* (1973) showed that stomatal resistance was smaller in air with sulphur dioxide than in sulphur dioxide free air, but Bull & Mansfield (1974) and Watson (1974) showed that rates of photosynthesis decreased when plants were exposed to sulphur dioxide.

Interpretation of these apparently conflicting results is difficult because the plant responses depend not only on the concentration and duration of exposure to a pollutant gas but also on environmental factors such as light, temperature and humidity, and on physiological factors such as species, age, previous history, nutritional and water status. To separate the response of plants to their physical environment from physiological changes induced by pollutants requires careful design of experimental systems, adequate specification of environmental conditions and appropriate quantitative analysis of results. More attention to these basic principles would enable results from different experiments to be compared, and conclusions syn-thesised. Such work would be more likely to identify the mechanisms of plant responses to air pollutants than many of the descriptive and non-analytical approaches that have been used in the past.

In this paper we discuss the physical principles by which gases are ex-changed between plants and the atmosphere. We describe a form of analysis which enables environmental factors governing rates of gas exchange to be separated from physiological factors and we outline experimental techniques useful in such analyses.

Resistance analogues in gas exchange

In describing gas exchange between plants and the atmosphere it is useful to regard the flux of a gas as being driven by a potential difference (difference in gas concentration) and limited by a resistance, so by analogy with Ohm's Law,

$$\text{flux} = \frac{\text{potential difference}}{\text{resistance}}. \tag{1}$$

An appropriate example is the flux, E, of water vapour (i.e. transpiration rate) from a leaf through the stomata. The potential difference driving the flux is the difference between the water vapour concentrations χ_1 in the stomatal cavity and the water vapour concentration χ in the atmosphere. It will be shown later that the limiting resistance, r, is the sum of a component describing properties of the air flow around the leaf and a component related to the dimensions of the stomata. Equation (1) becomes, for this case,

$$E = \frac{\chi_1 - \chi}{r}. \tag{2}$$

Equation (2) shows that E may vary either because the potential difference varies or because of changes in r. If the potential difference is known, then studies of effects of a pollutant on r give information from which transpiration rates in other environments can be predicted.

Resistance analogues have been widely used in recent years in analysing exchanges of carbon dioxide and water vapour between the atmosphere and leaves in enclosures (Gaastra, 1959; Chartier, 1970) or crops in the field (Monteith, 1963; Sceicz, van Bavel & Takami, 1973; Biscoe, Cohen & Wallace, 1975). Spedding (1969) and Biscoe et al. (1973) interpreted results of laboratory experiments with plants in polluted air in terms of resistance analogues and similar analyses were applied to field data by Garland, Clough & Fowler (1973) and Fowler & Unsworth (1974). Waggoner (1971) and Bennett, Hill & Gates (1973) use resistance analogues to model uptake of air pollutants by plants, but in general the potential of resistance analogues has not yet been recognised by the majority of plant physiologists concerned with air pollution effects.

The form of analysis allows distinction to be made between resistances which are functions of the aerodynamic properties of the experimental system and resistances which describe physiological or surface properties of plants. For water vapour, carbon dioxide and pollutant gases, several sections of the resistance pathway between the atmosphere and the plant are common, so that measurements of the transfer of one gas can be used to determine additional resistances limiting the transfer of other gases. Sestak, Catsky & Jarvis (1971) comprehensively reviewed the component resistances and described experimental procedures for determining resistances of single leaves and of crop canopies. Only a few common techniques applicable to enclosures will be described here.

Fig. 1 shows a transverse section through a typical leaf and gives the

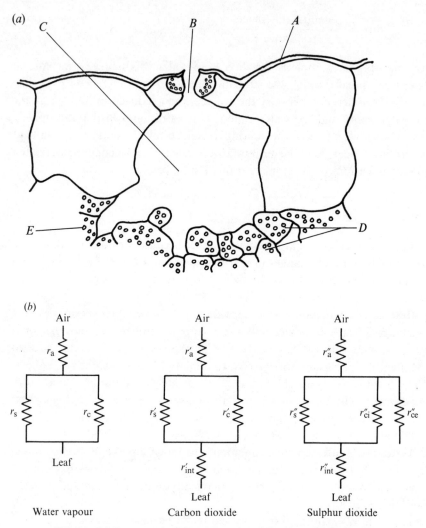

Fig. 1. (a) Cross-section through a stoma showing A, cuticle; B, stomatal throat; C, substomatal cavity; D, mesophyll cells; E, chloroplast.
(b) Resistance analogues for transfer of water vapour, carbon dioxide and sulphur dioxide between the atmosphere and a leaf. r_a, aerodynamic resistance; r_s, stomatal resistance; r_c, cuticular resistance; r_{int}, internal resistance. For further explanation see text.

analogue resistance chains describing exchange of water vapour, carbon dioxide and sulphur dioxide between a leaf and the atmosphere.

The total resistance, r, restricting the transfer of an entity is found by combining resistances according to the rules $r = r_1 + r_2 \ldots$ for resistances in series and $1/r = (1/r_1) + (1/r_2) \ldots$ for resistances in parallel (note that if

r_2 is much greater than r_1, $1/r \simeq 1/r_1$). Knowledge of the physical and physiological factors determining resistances clarifies the importance of alternative pathways.

Aerodynamic resistance

Diffusion of gases takes place by turbulent (eddy) diffusion in the free atmosphere where diffusion rates are identical for all gases. In a thin boundary layer close to the leaf there is a transition from turbulent to molecular diffusion, a much less efficient transfer process, and this has two consequences. First, the main aerodynamic resistance to transfer between the atmosphere and the leaf surface arises in the boundary layer and second, the resistance differs for different gases. In forced convection, when flow in the boundary layer is laminar, the aerodynamic resistance is proportional to $D^{-\frac{2}{3}}$, where D is the molecular diffusion coefficient of the gas in air (Thom, 1968; Monteith, 1973). This means that in Fig. 1(b):

$$r_a : r_a' : r_a'' = 1:1.39:1.57, \tag{3}$$

(based on numerical values of D for CO_2 and water vapour at 20 °C from Monteith (1973) and assuming that $DSO_2 = DCO_2[MCO_2/MSO_2]^{\frac{1}{2}}$ where M is the molecular weight).

For brevity, values of resistances common to several gases will refer to water vapour throughout this paper; the conversion factors in equation (3) should be applied to find corresponding aerodynamic resistances to carbon dioxide and sulphur dioxide transfer.

In enclosures, r_a is determined frequently by measuring the evaporation of water from a model leaf constructed so that there are no additional internal resistances to evaporation. Green blotting paper, or plaster of Paris models soaked in water are commonly used (Sestak et al., 1971). The evaporation rate E (g m^{-2} s^{-1}) is determined either by weighing the model or by measuring the flow rate and water vapour concentration of the air entering and leaving the chamber. In applying equation (2), the potential difference is the difference between the water vapour concentration (absolute humidity) in the chamber χ (g m^{-3}) and the water vapour concentration χ_1 (g m^{-3}) at the surface of the model leaf. χ_1 is found by measuring the leaf temperature and assuming that the air is saturated at the 'leaf' surface. Then

$$E = \frac{\chi_1 - \chi}{r_a}, \tag{4}$$

from which r_a (s m^{-1}) may be found. Precise measurement of leaf temperature is the main experimental difficulty in this technique.

In field crops, r_a, interpreted as a bulk aerodynamic resistance of the crop surface, is generally in the range 10–30 s m^{-1}. In plant and leaf chambers r_a may be very large in the absence of mechanical mixing especially if flow rates of air through the chamber are small. In such cases r_a may be much larger than other resistances in the transfer chain and so rates of photosynthesis, transpiration or uptake of a pollutant gas will be determined almost completely by this physical resistance and scarcely influenced by physiological changes. Fig. 2 shows the dependence of values of r_a for a

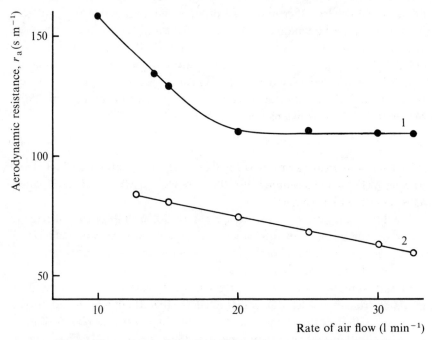

Fig. 2.   Dependence of aerodynamic resistance, r_a, of a model leaf in a cubical chamber, side 0.5 m, on the rate of flow of air through the chamber. 1, with no additional mixing; 2, with mechanical mixing by a fan.

single model leaf on flow rate of air through a cubical chamber of side 0.5 m. The introduction of a fan to increase turbulence reduced r_a to 60 s m^{-1}. Smaller leaf chambers equipped with fans may give values of r_a as low as 10 s m^{-1}.

Stomatal resistance

Gases diffuse through stomatal pores and across the substomatal cavity by the process of molecular diffusion. Consequently stomatal resistances are inversely proportional to molecular diffusion coefficients, i.e. in Fig. 1, at 20 °C:

$$r_s : r_s' : r_s'' = 1 : 1.65 : 1.98. \tag{5}$$

Stomatal resistances of leaves may be calculated from a knowledge of the dimensions and the distribution over the leaf of individual stomata (Penman & Schofield, 1951; Meidner & Mansfield, 1968). Alternatively, porometers (reviewed by Sestak et al., 1971) enable rapid measurements of r_s to be made in chambers and in the field. Another method, suitable for chambers, applies equation (2) to describe evaporation from real leaves. Rate of evaporation, water vapour concentration in the chamber and leaf temperature are measured. Then, using the same notation as equation (4), reference to the resistance chain in Fig. 1(b) shows that:

$$E = \frac{\chi_1 - \chi}{r_s + r_a}, \tag{6}$$

assuming that the walls in the substomatal cavity are covered with a free water surface at leaf temperature T_1. Knowing $r_s + r_a$ from equation (6), and measuring r_a by the method described earlier, r_s may be found.

To avoid the difficulty of measuring leaf temperature, transpiration rates may be expressed as a function of available energy H (W m^{-2}) at the leaf surface (e.g. measured with a net-radiometer), air temperature T (°C) and vapour pressure e (mbar) in the chamber, and resistances r_s and r_a, using the combination formula derived by Monteith (1965) in the form

$$E = \frac{\Delta H + [\rho c_p (e_s(T) - e)/r_a]}{\lambda \{\Delta + \gamma [1 + (r_s/r_a)]\}}, \tag{7}$$

where Δ is the slope of the curve of saturation vapour pressure of water versus temperature (mbar °C^{-1}), ρ air density (g m^{-3}), c_p specific heat of air (J g^{-1} °C^{-1}), $e_s(T)$ saturation vapour pressure (mbar) at chamber air temperature T, γ the psychrometric constant (mbar °C^{-1}) and λ the latent heat of vaporisation of water (J g^{-1}). Values of ρ, c_p, Δ, e_s, γ and λ were tabulated by Monteith (1973). Equation (7) offers an alternative method of determining r_s when all other factors are measured or known.

Values of r_s depend on species, leaf age and previous history; the rapid responses of r_s to changes in environmental factors such as water stress, light and carbon dioxide concentration were reviewed by Meidner & Mansfield (1968) and Raschke (1975). Stomatal resistances also respond to many pollutant gases, e.g. sulphur dioxide (Majernik & Mansfield, 1971; Biscoe et al., 1973), ozone (Hill & Littlefield, 1969) and British smog (Mansfield & Heath, 1963). For many species, when irradiance is large and there is no water stress, minimum values of r_s lie in the range 50–500 s m^{-1}.

Cuticular and surface resistance

From the leaf surface there are several alternative pathways for gas transfer which may be treated as resistances in parallel; (i) through stomata (ii) through the cuticle, and (iii) on to the exterior of the cuticle. Transfer takes place by gaseous and by liquid diffusion to different sites for different gases and consequently there are no physical relationships between resistances comparable with equations (3) and (5).

Resistances to carbon dioxide transfer through the cuticle are large because of the long pathway to chloroplasts in mesophyll cells (Fig. 1a). Consequently r_c' is usually ignored in comparison with the parallel resistance r_s'. Cuticular resistances to water vapour transfer usually lie in the range 10^3–10^5 s m^{-1} (Sestak et al., 1971) and again may often be ignored in comparison with r_s.

Sulphur dioxide may diffuse through the cuticle in gaseous phase (r_{ci}'') or it may be sorbed on to the external surface of the cuticle r_{ce}'', where it may react either with chemical compounds making up the cuticle or with a thin film of water on the cuticle. The limited evidence available suggests that the total cuticular resistance, r_c'', to sulphur dioxide transfer in plants is sometimes much less than the corresponding resistances for water vapour and carbon dioxide transfer. D. Fowler (personal communication) found that after exposing plants of Vicia faba with open stomata to $^{35}SO_2$ at concentrations of 150–200 μg m^{-3}, about 40% of the total ^{35}S content of the leaves could be removed by washing leaves with distilled water immediately after exposure, suggesting that surface capture was an effective process. From his analysis of results of recent field experiments over a crop of winter wheat, Fowler suggests that bulk cuticular resistance may have been only double the bulk 'stomatal' resistance for sulphur dioxide transfer. However, laboratory experiments by Spedding (1969) indicated that r_c'' for detached leaves of barley ranged from 3×10^3 to 2×10^5 s m^{-1}, increasing as relative humidity decreased. Relative magnitudes of r_{ci}'' and r_{ce}'' are not known at present.

Internal resistance

The walls of the substomatal cavity are usually assumed saturated with water and so there is no extra resistance for water vapour transfer. Carbon dioxide, however, has a further pathway for liquid phase transfer to carboxylation sites in chloroplasts of mesophyll cells. In spite of conceptual difficulties, the resistance of this pathway is often expressed as a diffusion resistance and subdivided into further resistances (see Sestak et al., 1971), but for the present purposes we will avoid such controversial topics and call the residual internal resistance to carbon dioxide transfer r_{int}'.

Sulphur dioxide is probably rapidly oxidised to sulphite on the wall of the substomatal cavity and r_{int}'' may be negligible when plants are able to transfer or convert the sulphite at the same rate as it is formed. On occasions when plants are exposed for long periods to sulphur dioxide, or when growth is slow, it seems likely that water in the substomatal cavity could become almost saturated with sulphite and so the internal resistance r_{int}'' would be very large. We have not found measurements of r_{int}'' in the literature.

For carbon dioxide, values of r_{int}' may most easily be determined by ensuring that the irradiance of a leaf is sufficient to give maximum (i.e. light-saturated) rates of gross photosynthesis, P_{max}. In such cases, assuming that the carbon dioxide concentration at the carboxylation sites is zero, and that cuticular resistance is infinitely large,

$$P_{max} = \frac{\Phi - 0}{r_a' + r_s' + r_{int}'} \tag{8}$$

where Φ (g m^{-3}) is the carbon dioxide concentration in the leaf chamber. Knowing r_a' and r_s', r_{int}' may be found. In chamber experiments and in the atmosphere, net photosynthesis, P_N, is usually measured and estimates of the carbon dioxide efflux, R, due to dark and light respiration must be made to derive $P_{max} = P_N + R$ (Chartier, 1970). Values of r_{int}' when light is not restricting photosynthesis are usually in the range 500–1000 s m^{-1} (Sestak et al., 1971).

Influence of resistances on rates of photosynthesis and transpiration

To illustrate the relative importance of r_a, r_s and r_{int}' in determining gas exchange, we will consider a typical leaf chamber experiment. Assume that the irradiance of the leaf saturates photosynthesis, i.e. $P = P_{max}$, that cuticular resistances to water vapour and carbon dioxide transfer are infinitely large, and that environmental conditions in the chamber are:

$H = 100$ W m^{-2}
$e = 12$ mbar
$T = 20\,°C$
$\Phi = 0.55$ g m^{-3} (300 ppm by volume)

From T, tables gives $e_s(T) = 23.4$ mbar, $\Delta = 1.45$ mbar °C^{-1}, and $\gamma = 0.66$ mbar °C^{-1}. Line A of Table 1 shows typical values of resistances measured by Littleton (1971) in a well-designed chamber enclosing single leaves of barley. Values of transpiration rates (E) and photosynthesis rates (P)

calculated from equations (7) and (8) are also shown in line A. Line B illus-trates the effect of inadequate turbulent mixing giving $r_a = 200$ s m^{-1}. Com-pared with A, evaporation is reduced by 22% and photosynthesis by 20%. The similarity of the reductions is quite coincidental because, whereas P always decreases as r_a increases, the variation of E with r_a depends on the relative magnitudes of r_s and of the ratio $\rho c_p(e_s - e)/\gamma H$ (Monteith, 1965). Monteith's analysis may be used to show that, for the conditions specified in Table 1, E would *increase* with increasing r_a if r_s had exceeded 300 s m^{-1}.

Table 1.   *Values of resistances* r_a, r_s *and* r_{int}', *and corresponding rates of transpiration and photosynthesis for three hypothetical experimental situations*

	r_a (s m^{-1})	r_s (s m^{-1})	r_{int}' (s m^{-1})	E g H$_2$O m^{-2} h^{-1}	P g CO$_2$ m^{-2} h^{-1}
A	10	200	700	147	1.91
B	200	200	700	114	1.53
C	10	160	700	187	2.03

Line C of Table 1 shows a hypothetical example of a situation where the action of an air pollutant decreases r_s by 20%, the size of the decrease observed by Biscoe *et al.* (1973). In this case, compared with line A, E increases by 27% but P increases only by 6%, illustrating the dominant control of P by r_{int}'. There is experimental evidence that P is either unchanged or *decreases* slightly at low sulphur dioxide concentrations (Bull & Mansfield, 1974; Watson, 1974) and in line C this would require r_{int}' to be increased by the action of the pollutant until it was equal to or greater than 780 s m^{-1}.

Equations (7) and (8) and the examples in Table 1 show that in experiments designed to investigate effects of air pollutants on gas exchange, environ-mental conditions must be carefully controlled. If r_a is excessively large, photosynthesis and transpiration rates will be relatively unaffected by changes in physiological resistances. Equation (7) shows that, even if no physiological responses to pollution occur, E may vary between treatments if T, H or the saturation deficit, $(e_s - e)$, vary. Conversely, a physiological response such as stomatal opening (i.e. a reduction in r_s) may be masked by a consequent increase in chamber vapour pressure decreasing the saturation deficit, and so reducing the potential difference driving evaporation.

With adequately designed experiments the analysis of results in terms of resistance analogues enables effects of pollutants on gaseous diffusion resistances to be isolated from effects on internal resistances, and this may prove a profitable approach for linking with and for directing research at cellular and at biochemical levels.

References

Bell, J. N. B. & Clough, W. S. (1973). Depression in yield of ryegrass exposed to SO_2. *Nature, London* **241**, 47–9.

Bennett, J. H., Hill, A. C. & Gates, D. M. (1973). A model for gaseous pollutant sorption by leaves. *Journal of the Air Pollution Control Association* **23**, 957–62.

Biscoe, P. V., Cohen, H. & Wallace, J. S. (1975). Daily and seasonal changes of water potential in cereals. *Proceedings of the Royal Society of London*, in press.

Biscoe, P. V., Unsworth, M. H. & Pinckney, H. R. (1973). The effects of low concentrations of sulphur dioxide on stomatal behaviour in *Vicia faba*. *New Phytologist* **72**, 1299–1306.

Bleasdale, J. K. A. (1973). Effects of coal smoke pollutant gases on the growth of ryegrass. *Environmental Pollution* **5**, 275–85.

Bull, J. N. & Mansfield, T. A. (1974). Photosynthesis in leaves exposed to SO_2 and NO_2. *Nature, London* **250**, 443–4.

Chartier, P. (1970) A model of CO_2 assimilation in the leaf. In *Prediction and measurement of photosynthetic productivity*, pp. 307–15. PUDOC, Centre for Agricultural Publishing and Documentation, Wageningen.

Cowling, D. W., Jones, L. H. P. & Lockyer, D. R. (1973). Increased yield through correction of sulphur deficiency in ryegrass exposed to SO_2. *Nature, London* **243**, 479–80.

Daines, R. H. (1968). Sulphur dioxide and plant response. *Journal of Occupational Medicine* **10**, 516–26.

Fowler, D. & Unsworth, M. H. (1974). Dry deposition of sulphur dioxide on wheat. *Nature, London* **249**, 389–90.

Gaastra, P. (1959). Photosynthesis of crop plants as influenced by light, carbon dioxide, temperature and stomatal diffusion resistance. *Mededelingen van de Landbouwhogeschool te Wageningen* **59** (13), 1–68.

Garland, J. A., Clough, W. S. & Fowler, D. (1973). Deposition of sulphur dioxide on grass. *Nature, London* **242**, 256–7.

Hill, A. C. & Littlefield, N. (1969). Ozone. Effect on apparent photosynthesis, rate of transpiration and stomatal closure in plants. *Environmental Science and Technology* **3**, 52–6.

Katz, M. (1949). Sulphur dioxide in the atmosphere and its relation to plant life. *Industrial and Engineering Chemistry* **41**, 2450–65.

Littleton, E. J. (1971). The gas exchange of barley leaves and ears. PhD thesis, University of Nottingham School of Agriculture.

Majernik, O. & Mansfield, T. A. (1971). Effects of SO_2 pollution on stomatal movements in *Vicia faba*. *Phytopathologische Zeitschrift, Berlin* **71**, 123–8.

Mansfield, T. A. & Heath, O. V. S. (1963). An effect of 'smog' on stomatal behaviour. *Nature, London* **200**, 596.

Meidner, H. & Mansfield, T. A. (1968). *Physiology of stomata.* McGraw-Hill, New York.

Monteith, J. L. (1963). Gas exchange in plant communities. In *Environmental control of plant growth*, Ed. L. T. Evans, pp. 95–112. Academic Press, New York & London.

Monteith, J. L. (1965). Evaporation and environment. *Symposia of the Society for Experimental Biology* 19, 205–34.

Monteith, J. L. (1973). *Principles of environmental physics.* Edward Arnold, London.

Pahlich, E. (1975). Effect of SO_2-pollution on cellular regulation. A general concept of the mode of action of gaseous air contamination. *Atmospheric Environment* 9, 261–3.

Penman, H. L. & Schofield, R. K. (1951). Some physical aspects of assimilation and transpiration. *Symposia of the Society for Experimental Biology* 5, 115–29.

Raschke, K. (1975). Stomatal action. *Annual Review of Plant Physiology* 26, in press.

Sceicz, G., van Bavel, C. H. M. & Takami, S. (1973). Stomatal factor in the water use and dry matter production by sorghum. *Agricultural Meteorology* 12, 361–89.

Sestak, Z., Catsky, J. & Jarvis, P. G. (eds) (1971). *Plant photosynthetic production; manual of methods.* W. Junk, The Hague.

Sij, J. W. & Swanson, C. A. (1974). Short-term kinetic studies on the inhibition of photosynthesis by sulfur dioxide. *Journal of Environmental Quality* 3, 103–7.

Spedding, D. J. (1969). Uptake of sulphur dioxide by barley leaves at low sulphur dioxide concentrations. *Nature, London* 224, 1229–30.

Thom, A. S. (1968). The exchange of momentum, mass and heat between an artificial leaf and the air-flow in a wind-tunnel. *Quarterly Journal of the Royal Meteorological Society* 94, 44–55.

Thomas, M. D. (1961). Effects of air pollution on plants. In *Air pollution, WHO monograph series No. 46*, pp. 233–78. WHO, Geneva.

Thomas, M. D. & Hill, G. K. (1937). Relation of sulphur dioxide in the atmosphere to photosynthesis and respiration in Alfalfa. *Plant Physiology* 12, 309–83.

Waggoner, P. E. (1971). Plants and polluted air. *Bioscience* 21, 455–9.

Watson, R. L. (1974). Effects of sulphur dioxide on photosynthetic rates of maize and field beans. BSc dissertation, University of Nottingham School of Agriculture.

Wellburn, A. R., Majernik, O. & Wellburn, F. A. M. (1972). Effects of SO_2 and NO_2 polluted air on the ultrastructure of chloroplasts. *Environmental Pollution* 3, 37–49.

A.W.DAVISON & J.BLAKEMORE

Factors determining fluoride accumulation in forage

Review and introduction

Fluoride accumulation by plants has attracted the attention of research workers for three main reasons. The first is that vegetation acts as an important sink for air pollutants. Gases penetrate vegetation canopies rapidly (Bennett & Hill, 1973) and are absorbed in relation to their solubility in water. For example, Hill (1971) showed that an alfalfa canopy removed gases in the order hydrogen fluoride > sulphur dioxide > chlorine > nitrogen dioxide > ozone > PAN (peroxyacyl nitrates) > nitric oxide > carbon monoxide. In Bennett & Hill's (1973) experiments a hydrogen fluoride concentration of 5 pphm $(= 40.1\,\mu\text{g m}^{-3})$ above a 40-cm high alfalfa canopy was reduced to about 1 pphm $(= 8.03\,\mu\text{g m}^{-3})$ at 10 cm above soil level. The efficiency of vegetation in absorbing pollutants is such that it can produce pockets of relatively clean air (Gilbert, 1968) where sensitive species can persist. In addition, it has been suggested (Bernatsky, 1969) that green belts might help to reduce air pollution.

The second reason for interest in the subject is that fluorides absorbed by leaves can be phytotoxic, and plants are more sensitive to fluorides than to other air pollutants (Jacobson, Weinstein, McCune & Hitchcock, 1966). Sensitive varieties of certain species are visibly injured by exposure to concentrations less than $0.6\,\mu\text{g m}^{-3}$ (Compton & Remmert, 1960). The fluoride concentrates in the margins and tips of the leaves and produces chlorosis, distortion, buckling, savoying, or necrosis (NAS, 1971). The concentration of fluoride in the tissues needed to cause injury depends on the rate of accumulation of the element, the species, variety, stage of growth and the environmental conditions. Consequently, it is usually impossible to define a threshold concentration above which injury always occurs and it is quite common to find apparently anomalous situations such as injured leaves with a lower fluoride content than adjacent uninjured leaves.

The third reason for the interest is that fluorides accumulated by plants can cause dental and osseous lesions, and lameness in grazing animals. The order of sensitivity of farm animals is dairy cows > beef cows > sheep > swine > chickens > turkeys (NAS, 1971). Suttie (1969) proposed that in order to protect livestock the fluoride content of forage, sampled on a monthly basis, should not exceed 40 μg g^{-1} dry wt averaged over the year or be in excess of 60 μg g^{-1} for more than two consecutive months, or in excess of 80 μg g^{-1} for more than one month. Because of lack of knowledge of the factors affecting accumulation these forage concentrations cannot be specified in terms of air concentrations at the present time (McCune & Hitchcock, 1970).

A growing pasture or meadow sward is a complex system containing leaves, stems, flowers and fruits of different age, stage of development, surface characteristics and rate of growth. Furthermore the environment – humidity, temperature, light, wind speed and concentration of pollutant – varies throughout the sward, so it is not surprising that accumulation and the factors that affect the process are so poorly understood. McCune & Hitchcock (1970) recognised seven major groups of factors that can affect the concentration of fluoride found in vegetation: the physical and chemical form of the fluoride; adsorption, uptake and loss of fluorides from the plant; the dose and frequency of fumigation; environmental factors; biological factors such as the species or variety; sampling procedure; and the analytical procedure. Considering the first of these, fluorides may be present in the air in gaseous or particulate form. By far the commonest gaseous form is hydrogen fluoride (HF) but particulates vary in size, chemical composition and solubility. Accumulation from particulates has been much less studied than that from hydrogen fluoride. In experiments with submicrometre particulates, Less, Arthur & McGregor (1974) found that the rate of accumulation by perennial ryegrass (*Lolium perenne*) was very low, being only about 1% of that from an equivalent concentration of hydrogen fluoride. McCune, Hitchcock, Jacobson & Weinstein (1965) used larger (2–4 μm) particulates and found two- to fivefold increases in fluoride content depending on the species and dose. Between 70 and 100% of the fluoride accumulated from particulates is removable (Pack, Hill, Thomas & Transtrum, 1959; McCune *et al.*, 1965) by a mild detergent wash, indicating that little penetrates to the interior of the leaf. This lack of penetration is the reason why particulate forms do not cause significant injury to plants (Pack *et al.*, 1959; McCune *et al.*, 1965). On the other hand as particulates can contribute to fluorosis in grazing animals accumulation from this source must still be given consideration.

Fumigation under controlled conditions, washing of leaves with a variety of solvents, and analysis of different tissues (Jacobson *et al.*, 1966) have shown that in contrast to particulate forms, hydrogen fluoride is both adsorbed on the outer surfaces and penetrates to the interior of the leaf via the stomata. Inside the leaf it is mostly concentrated in the margins and tips but a proportion moves outwards towards the surface (Jacobson *et al.*, 1966). It is presumed that this can lead to a loss of fluoride by weathering. Numerous experiments (NAS, 1971) suggest that accumulation is related to the concentration of the gas and the duration of fumigation, and therefore that accumulation can be described by an equation of the type $\Delta F = KCT$, where ΔF is the change in plant fluoride in $\mu g\,g^{-1}$ dry wt, K is an accumulation coefficient, C is the concentration of hydrogen fluoride in $\mu g\,m^{-3}$, and T is the duration of fumigation in days. The accumulation coefficient, K, depends on the species and possibly the concentration of fluoride in the air and the duration of the fumigation (NAS, 1971). Estimates of K for a range of species under different experimental conditions vary from less than 1 to over 9 (NAS, 1971). This implies that without taking account of losses due to weathering or leaf abscission, or to growth dilution, exposure of a plant to $1\,\mu g\,F\,m^{-3}$ would lead to accumulation of from about 1 to $9\,\mu g\,F\,g^{-1}$ dry wt per day of exposure. There are few estimates of the rate of loss of fluorides from leaves, but in the case of alfalfa Hitchcock *et al.* (1971) found that the concentration during a post-fumigation period decreased by 50% in 8 to 22 days in different experiments. The loss was attributed partly to weathering and partly to growth dilution.

Environmental factors can also exert an important effect on accumulation. Benedict, Ross & Wade (1965) showed that alfalfa plants fumigated in the dark accumulated less fluoride than those in the light, and in the former case most of the fluoride was adsorbed on the outer surfaces of the leaves. The same authors showed that temperature affected accumulation and transport of fluoride within the plant, though the temperatures used were considerably higher than any that would be experienced by plants growing in the field in the UK. Rainfall could affect the fluoride content of plants in several ways but it is one of the least-investigated factors. It might wash fluorides out of the air, deposit dissolved ions or suspended particulates on leaves, wash ions or particulates from leaves, or affect the adsorptive capacity of the leaf surface. Allcroft, Burns & Hebert (1965) noted a highly significant negative correlation between the fluoride content of pastures and rainfall, which suggests that the rain was either scrubbing appreciable quantities of fluoride from the air or washing it from leaves. An effect on adsorption was suggested by the experiments of Less *et al.* (1974) who found that simulated rain in greenhouses brought about a twofold increase in fluoride accumulation by perennial ryegrass.

Among the biological factors that can affect accumulation species and variety are the best known, but sward structure (Hill, 1971) and the stage of development could be equally important. One effect of development is illustrated in Fig. 1. The topmost leaves of barley plants growing in an area subject to emissions from domestic fires (Davison, Rand & Betts, 1973) were

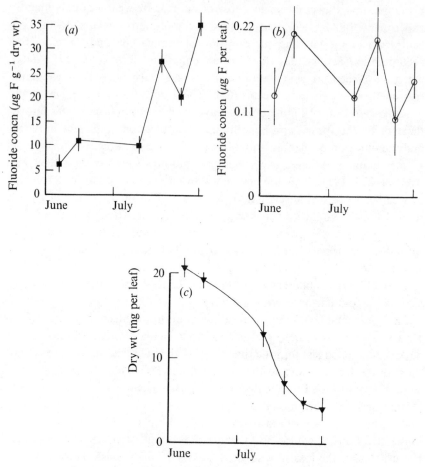

Fig. 1.   Analysis of barley leaves collected at intervals during June and July, 1973. (a) Fluoride concentration in leaves in μg F g^{-1} dry wt; (b) fluoride content in μg F per barley leaf; (c) dry weight in mg per barley leaf. Vertical bars indicate 95% confidence intervals.

sampled at intervals, dried, weighed and analysed. As Fig. 1 shows, the fluoride concentration (μg F g^{-1} dry wt) rose steeply in July by a factor of about five but this was not due to continued accumulation of fluoride because the quantity of fluoride per leaf, although subject to considerable variance, did not show a similar upward trend. The apparent increase in concentration was caused by a fivefold loss of dry weight due to ripening and senescence. This phenomenon has been observed several times with cereal leaves but does not appear to occur in the case of ash (*Fraxinus excelsior*) or hawthorn (*Crataegus monogyna*).

The final but by no means the least important factors that can affect the observed accumulation are sampling and analysis. Pastures are usually mixtures of species which vary in height, distribution within the sward and in density. In addition hedgerows, fences and trees create variation in airborne fluoride concentrations and in environmental conditions, so that spatial variation within a pasture is always high. Unless sampling is rigorously carried out this factor can have an important affect on the observed concentration. Similarly, fluoride analysis is still notoriously troublesome and there are often major discrepancies between laboratories (Jacobson & McCune, 1969). McCune & Hitchcock (1970) suggested that the analytical system should be an integral part of the statistical design and analysis of the experiment.

One of the problems in assessing the factors that affect accumulation is that most of the work has been done under controlled conditions, mostly with hydrogen fluoride in the absence of any particulate form, often with plants growing in isolation rather than in a sward, and usually in the absence of environmental factors such as rain, wind and pathogens. In an attempt to obtain more information about field events the authors (Davison, Blakemore & Wright, unpublished data) re-examined some data of Allcroft et al. (1965). This showed that statistical analysis of ambient fluoride levels and of environmental factors could yield useful information about the effects of factors such as rain, so a series of experiments was set up at sites in north-east England. Each site is subjected to emissions from a number of sources so the concentration of gaseous and particulate fluorides varies with time and, in particular, with wind direction. Facilities are available at each site for recording airborne fluorides, grass fluoride, rain and temperature. Experimental grass and grass/clover plots enable species differences and the effects of sward structure to be investigated. A rain simulator (on loan from the National Institute of Agricultural Engineering) and open-ended cloches can be positioned over the plots. Two experiments have been completed, one involving daily sampling and lasting 30 days, the other using weekly sampling and lasting 30 weeks. The first experiment is described in this paper. It was designed to investigate the sampling interval, because if there is a relationship between two factors such as airborne and grass fluorides, and sampling is at very short intervals, any pattern could be obscured by sampling and analytical errors. As the sampling interval is increased the duration of experiments becomes unacceptable, so the optimum interval should lie somewhere between the extremes. One day was chosen as the minimum practical sampling interval and the daily data were averaged to give information for 2-, 3- and 4-day intervals.

Materials and methods

Air and grass samples were taken daily over a 30-day period lasting from 4 October 1974 to 4 November 1974. Replicated samples of grass were cut with shears from $1\,m \times 1\,m$ plots consisting primarily of *Lolium perenne* (S24) sown in spring 1974. Half of each sample was washed (Jacobson *et al.*, 1966) before drying at 105 °C. Dried material was ground in a Casella mill and the fluoride content determined using an Orion specific ion-electrode. Airborne fluorides were collected and separated by drawing air through two successive impregnated filter papers (Weinstein & Mandl, 1971) in an open-face holder mounted 50 cm above ground level. Precipitation was collected in a standard copper rain gauge fitted with a polythene collecting vessel. All collecting surfaces were coated with polyurethane paint.

Results

The mean 24-hour gaseous and particulate fluoride concentrations over the 30-day period were 0.54 and $0.43\,\mu g\,F\,m^{-3}$ respectively. Particulate concentrations were more variable than gaseous: standard deviation/mean for particulates was 0.88; standard deviation/mean for gaseous fluoride 0.67. The average rainfall on the 17 rain days was 3.52 mm. Temperatures were unusually high for November and there was visible grass growth.

In order to distinguish between fluoride inside the leaves and that deposited or adsorbed on the surface, half of each sample was given a mild detergent wash. The fluoride content of washed leaves will be considered first.

The daily variation in the fluoride content of washed grass is shown in Fig. 2. The variation between plots (indicated by the vertical bars) was

Table 1. *Correlations between the fluoride concentration in washed grass and environmental factors*

		1	2	3	4	5
1	Washed-grass F	—				
2	Air, gaseous F	0.604*	—			
3	Air, particulate F	0.491*	0.851*	—		
4	Rain	−0.364*	−0.253	−0.276	—	
5	Previous day's grass F	0.655*	0.326	0.359	−0.105	—

*Probability < 0.05.

considerable (average standard deviation/mean = 0.33) but there was never-theless significant day-to-day variation. On four days there was a significant increase compared with the previous day, the largest being 33 μg g^{-1} on the 24th/25th day. As the total airborne fluoride concentration never rose above 1 μg m^{-3} this suggests a greater rate of accumulation than would be

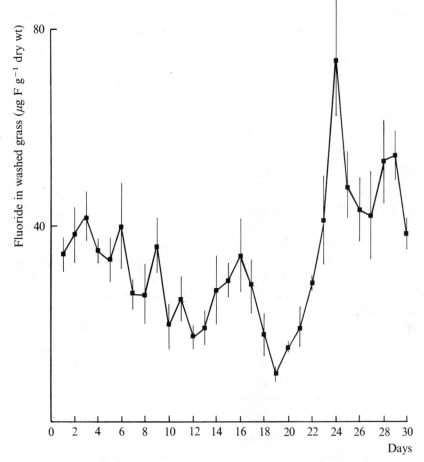

Fig. 2. Daily variation in the fluoride content (μg F g^{-1} dry wt) of grass previously washed with a mild detergent. Vertical bars indicate 95% confidence intervals.

expected from fumigation experiments under controlled conditions. On eight days there was a significant fall in the grass concentration indicating a considerable rate of weathering.

The simple correlation coefficients between the factors measured are given in Table 1. The washed-grass fluoride was significantly correlated with the concentration recorded in the washed grass on the previous day, with both gaseous and particulate concentrations, and with rainfall. In order to try to determine whether any of these were indirect, partial correlation coefficients were computed (Table 2). The first partials in Table 2, between washed-grass fluoride and both the previous day's washed-grass fluoride and rain, remained

Table 2.   *Partial correlation coefficients* (r) *between the fluoride concentration in washed grass and environmental factors*

	Simple correlation	r	Partial correlation controlling for:	r	P
1	Washed-grass F/previous day's grass F	0.655	Air, gaseous F; air, particulate F; rain	0.652	0.001
2	Washed-grass F/rain	−0.364	Air, gaseous F; air, particulate F; previous day's grass F	−0.358	0.039
3	Washed-grass F/air, gaseous F	0.604	Rain; air, particulate F; previous day's grass F	0.489	0.006
4	Washed-grass F/air, particulate F	0.491	Rain; air, gaseous F; previous day's grass F	−0.251	0.113

essentially the same, implying that they were direct correlations. The correlation with gaseous fluoride was reduced but still significant, indicating that this correlation was partly an indirect one. The correlation with particulate fluoride was non-significant when controlled for the previous day's grass fluoride, gaseous fluoride and rain, which indicates that it was probably indirect and therefore non-causal.

The effect of increasing the sampling interval was investigated by averaging the data for 2-, 3- and 4-day periods respectively. Simple regressions of washed-grass fluoride on gaseous fluoride with increasing sampling intervals are given in Table 3. Averaging the data in this way gave essentially the same

Table 3.   *Regression of the fluoride concentration in washed grass on gaseous fluoride, calculated using data averaged over 1-, 2-, 3- and 4-day periods, respectively*

		r	n	P
1-day	washed-grass F = 21.3 + 24.7 (gaseous F)	0.603	30	0.001
2-day average	washed-grass F = 20.7 + 25.4 (gaseous F)	0.652	15	0.02
3-day average	washed-grass F = 20.1 + 25.5 (gaseous F)	0.674	10	0.04
4-day average	washed-grass F = 18.0 + 27.7 (gaseous F)	0.797	7	0.05

regression equation but gradually decreased the variance and increased the correlation coefficient.

Stepwise multiple regressions of grass fluoride on the other variables were also calculated for 1-, 2- and 3-day periods (Table 4). The multiple regression

Table 4. *Stepwise multiple regression of the fluoride concentration in washed grass on various factors, calculated using data averaged over 1-, 2- and 3-day periods*

		r	$r^2 \times 100$
1-day	grass F $= 10.02 + 25.0$ gaseous F $- 0.9$ rain $+ 0.525$ previous grass F $- 10$ particulate F	0.815	66.4
2-day	average grass F $= 13.01 + 36.8$ gaseous F $- 0.9$ rain $+ 0.481$ previous grass F $- 23$ particulate F	0.865	74.8
3-day	average grass F $= 20.29 + 42.8$ gaseous F $- 0.9$ rain $+ 0.284$ previous grass F $- 28$ particulate F	0.880	77.4

coefficient increased from 0.815 to 0.880, but more important, the regression constants for the previous period's washed-grass fluoride and for gaseous fluoride showed a systematic change. The contribution of the previous period's grass fluoride to the equation gradually decreased while the contribution from the gaseous fluoride concentration showed a corresponding increase. This implied that over the space of only a few days the fluoride in the plant at the start of a sampling period becomes progressively less important in determining the fluoride content eventually observed.

The fluoride that was removable by washing the leaves (= external grass fluoride*) was calculated by subtracting the fluoride content of a washed subsample from that of an unwashed subsample. This external fluoride was even more variable than the washed-grass fluoride. However, there were significant correlations (Table 5) between the external grass fluoride and the previous day's external grass fluoride, gaseous fluoride, particulate fluoride and rain. The correlations between external fluoride and the three environmental factors gaseous fluoride, particulate fluoride and rain, were very similar to those between washed-grass fluoride and the same factors (see Table 1 for comparison). However, the correlation between the external fluoride and the previous day's external fluoride (0.431) was much lower than the corresponding correlation between washed-grass fluoride and the previous day's washed-grass fluoride (0.655). This was probably due

* This term is used for convenience. It is recognised that the fraction probably included not only surface deposits and adsorbed ions but also some internal fluoride.

to the external fluoride being superficial and therefore in a greater state of flux than the largely internal, washed-grass fluoride.

It had been anticipated that the external fluoride would be most strongly correlated with particulate fluoride but there was a higher correlation

Table 5. *Correlation coefficients between the external fluoride concentration of grass and other factors*

	Previous day's external fluoride	Gaseous fluoride	Particulate fluoride	Rain
External grass fluoride	0.431	0.600	0.513	−0.385
P	< 0.02	< 0.001	< 0.01	< 0.05

coefficient with gaseous fluoride, so partial correlations (Table 6) were calculated to determine whether there was any interaction between the environmental factors. The external grass fluoride/gaseous fluoride correlation remained significant ($P = 0.03$) when the effect of particulate fluoride and rain was removed, implying that there was a direct causal correlation, but

Table 6. *Partial correlation coefficients between the external fluoride concentration of grass and airborne fluoride*

Simple correlation	r	Partial correlation controlling for:		r	P
External grass F/gaseous F	0.600	1	Particulate F	0.364	0.03
		2	Particulate F, rain	0.370	0.03
External grass F/particulate F	0.513	1	Gaseous F	0.004	0.49
		2	Gaseous F, rain	−0.034	0.43

the external grass fluoride/particulate fluoride correlation disappeared completely when the effect of gaseous fluoride was removed. It appeared, therefore, that particulate fluoride did not make a major contribution to the external grass fluoride concentration.

The stepwise regression of external grass fluoride on gaseous fluorides, the previous day's external fluoride, rain and particulate fluoride accounted for only ($0.662^2 \times 100$) 43.8% of the variance, much lower than the corresponding regression for washed-grass fluoride (Table 4).

Discussion

The primary objective of the experiment was to determine the optimum sampling interval for collection of ambient fluoride and environmental data. As fumigation studies have suggested that exposure to $1 \, \mu g \, F \, m^{-3}$ for 1 day would lead to an increase in concentration of from 1 to $9 \, \mu g \, g^{-1}$ dry wt, it was anticipated that at a site where the air concentration was known to be lower than $1 \, \mu g \, m^{-3}$ a daily sampling interval would be too short because random sampling and analytical errors would mask daily increments. However, the results showed that day-to-day variation was measurable and as a result there were highly significant correlations between grass fluoride content and many of the environmental factors. Averaging data over 2 or more days smoothed out some of the variance but the correlations based on daily sampling were sufficiently high to conclude that it should be possible to investigate the effects of factors such as sward structure by means of intensive short-term experiments.

The variance between plots could have been due to variance in airborne fluorides, sward characteristics or to edge effects. No estimate of spatial variation in airborne fluorides was made but this was probably relatively small as all the plots were contained within a $5 \, m \times 5 \, m$ square. Although the plots were carefully sown and tended, there was some variation in height, particularly at the edges, and in the proportion of dead leaves present. This could have been important because in previous work in the area (A. W. Rand, unpublished data) it has been consistently found that dead leaves have a higher concentration than adjacent green leaves. The data in Table 7 are for samples collected in March 1971.

In the introduction it was pointed out that fumigation experiments with hydrogen fluoride show that the relationship between airborne fluoride and accumulation can apparently be described by an equation of the type $\Delta F = KCT$. If this simple relationship held in the field then the fluoride content of vegetation exposed to varying concentrations of airborne fluoride, in the absence of any losses, would tend to show a gradual increase. Losses due to weathering and other causes would partly or wholly balance gain and so the actual concentration would be expected to show a complex undulating pattern. In this situation the fluoride content of vegetation would not show a correlation with that in the air unless, as postulated by Hitchcock *et al.* (1971), gains were exactly balanced by losses. The fact that there was a correlation in the 30-day experiment indicates a difference between events in the laboratory and the field. In the field, there must have been equilibration between airborne and vegetation fluoride and at a rate faster than suggested

Table 7.   *The fluoride content (µg g^{-1} dry wt), of dead and green leaves of mixed grass species collected at ten sites in March 1971*

Site	Green	Dead	Dead/green
1	4	20	5.0
2	5	16	3.2
3	16	20	1.25
4	18	20	1.11
5	13	23	1.77
6	16	38	2.38
7	7	18	2.57
8	7	33	4.71
9	26	48	1.85
10	10	26	2.60
		Average =	2.64

by laboratory experiments. There are several differences between conditions in a controlled environment and the field which could have contributed to this difference, such as the surface characteristics of leaves, but rain stands out as being the most obvious and potentially the most important. The humid, November air could have increased adsorption (Less *et al.*, 1974), while rain itself could have both deposited and leached fluorides and therefore led to rapid gains and losses. If rain plays this central role in equilibration then correlations between airborne and vegetation fluorides should not be so pronounced in drier climates or seasons.

Pasture fluoride concentrations sometimes decrease (e.g. Allcroft *et al.*, 1965; Gründer, 1972) during early summer and this is usually thought to be due to dilution of the accumulated fluoride by new growth. As a result, it has been suggested (Allcroft *et al.*, 1965) that improving grass growth and increasing turnover can reduce pasture fluoride concentrations. However, the rapid rate of equilibration between airborne and grass fluoride found in the present experiment makes both of these conclusions questionable. It would appear that new growth would very quickly reach the same concentration as older leaves unless the surface characteristics and stomatal activity were radically different in adsorptive capacity. A programme of experiments using growth inhibitors and incorporating measurements of growth is being undertaken to investigate this problem.

Partial correlations showed that neither the washed-grass fluoride nor the external fluoride were strongly correlated with airborne particulates. As the particulates were not examined and measured it is difficult to add any further comment except that it is contrary to what might be expected from most published work (Pack *et al.*, 1959; McCune *et al.*, 1965) but in agreement with the findings of Less *et al.* (1974) who worked with submicrometre-sized material.

J. Blakemore gratefully acknowledges receipt of a CASE Studentship from the SRC.

References

Allcroft, R., Burns, K. N. & Hebert, C. N. (1965). *Fluorosis in cattle. II. Development and alleviation: experimental studies. Ministry of agriculture, fisheries and food, animal disease surveys report 2. Part II.* Her Majesty's Stationery Office, London. 58 pp.

Benedict, H. M., Ross, J. M. & Wade, R. H. (1965). Some responses of vegetation to atmospheric fluorides. *Journal of the Air Pollution Control Association* **15**, 253–5.

Bennett, J. H. & Hill, A. C. (1973). Absorption of gaseous air pollutants by a standardised plant canopy. *Journal of the Air Pollution Control Association* **23**, 203–6.

Bernatsky, A. (1969). Die Bedeutung von Schutzpflanzungen gegen Luftverunreinigungen. In *Air pollution. Proceedings of the first European congress on the influence of air pollution on plants and animals, Wageningen*, pp. 383–95. Centre for Agricultural Publishing and Documentation, Wageningen.

Compton, O. C. & Remmert, L. F. (1960). Effect of airborne fluorine on injury and fluorine content of *Gladiolius* leaves. *Proceedings of the American Society for Horticultural Science* **75**, 663–75.

Davison, A. W., Rand, A. W. & Betts, W. E. (1973). Measurement of atmospheric fluoride concentrations in urban areas. *Environmental Pollution* **5**, 23–33.

Gilbert, O. L. (1968). Biological indicators of air pollution. PhD thesis, University of Newcastle-upon-Tyne.

Gründer, H. D. (1972). Prevention or reduction of fluoride effects in cattle. *Fluoride* **2**, 74–81.

Hill, A. C. (1971). Vegetation: a sink for atmospheric pollutants. *Journal of the Air Pollution Control Association* **21**, 341–6.

Hitchcock, A. E., McCune, D. C., MacLean, D. C., Weinstein, L. H., Jacobson, J. S. & Mandl, R. H. (1971). Effects of hydrogen fluoride fumigation on alfalfa and orchard grass. *Contributions from the Boyce Thompson Institute* **24**, 363–85.

Jacobson, J. S., Weinstein, L. H., McCune, D. C. & Hitchcock, A. E. (1966). The accumulation of fluorine by plants. *Journal of the Air Pollution Control Association* **16**, 412–17.

Jacobson, J. S. & McCune, D. C. (1969). Interlaboratory study of analytical techniques for fluorine in vegetation. *Journal of the Association of Official Analytical Chemists* **52**, 894–9.

Less, L. N., Arthur, A. M. & McGregor, A. (1974). Fluorine uptake by grass from aluminium smelter fume. Paper presented to the Annual Meeting of the American Institute of Mechanical Engineers, Dallas, Texas.

McCune, D. C. & Hitchcock, A. E. (1970). Fluoride in forage: factors determining its accumulation from the atmosphere and concentration in the plant. *Proceedings of the Second International Clean Air Congress of the International Union of Air Pollution Prevention Associations*, pp. 289–92.

McCune, D. C., Hitchcock, A. E., Jacobson, J. S. & Weinstein, L. H. (1965). Fluoride accumulation and growth of plants exposed to particulate cryolite in the atmosphere. *Contributions from the Boyce Thompson Institute* **23**, 1–12.

NAS (1971). *Biologic effects of atmospheric pollutants: fluorides.* National Academy of Sciences, Washington. 295 pp.

Pack, M. R., Hill, A. C., Thomas, M. D. & Transtrum, L. G. (1959). Determination of gaseous and particulate inorganic fluorides in the atmosphere. *American Society Testing Materials Special Technical Publication* **281**, 27–44.

Suttie, J. W. (1969). *Air quality criteria to protect livestock from fluoride toxicity.* The Aluminium Association, New York. 23 pp.

Weinstein, L. H. & Mandl, R. H. (1971). The separation and collection of gaseous and particulate fluorides. *Verein Deutscher Ingenieure Berichte* **164**, 53–70.

D.C.McCUNE, D.C.MacLEAN
& R.E.SCHNEIDER

Experimental approaches to the effects of airborne fluoride on plants

Everyone is familiar with the cyclical progress of experimental science. New techniques beget new results, which then beget new techniques, and so it goes. Although experimentation on the response of plants to air pollutants follows this same course and logic, it must also address itself to the solution of some rather practical problems. Thus, applicability of results is as much a component of its progress as technique and knowledge.

The problems that must be answered through experimentation can be posed as simple questions. What are the effects of atmospheric fluoride on plants? How can these effects be identified and estimated? Under what circumstances are they likely to occur? What is necessary to prevent them? The practical uses of the answers to these questions are found in: the establishment of liability in claims for damages in litigation or arbitration; the promulgation of standards for emissions or air quality; and, the prediction of the probable or possible environmental consequences of a new source of fluoride or a change in operation of an existing one.

There are many different experimental approaches that can contribute to the answering of these questions. But the final link in the chain of evidence which leads from pollutant to effect is forged by field experimentation. The most common feature of this kind of experimentation is the enclosure of field-grown plants by chambers. A pollutant, such as hydrogen fluoride (HF), may be added at known dosages to the atmosphere in some chambers, or, an ambient pollutant or group of pollutants, such as photochemical oxidants, may be excluded from the atmosphere of some chambers. Thompson, Taylor, Thomas & Ivie (1967) used both approaches and their combination in a study of the effects of fluoride and oxidants on bearing citrus trees. However, these long-term experiments and others have shown that the enclosure of plants leads to problems: the development of abnormal abiotic and biotic environmental conditions. Among the former, the most serious are the entrapment of heat and the absence of precipitation, of the latter, the absence of pollinating insects and natural agents that normally control insect infestations on plants.

Fig. 1.   A view of the open-top chamber as used for field exposures with hydrogen fluoride. Two modules, each 1.2 m high, are used standardly for experiments. A plastic netting is secured over the top of the upper module. The white, louvred enclosure at left contains the hydrogen-fluoride-generator and pumps for air monitoring. Blower and air filter assemblies are mounted on the trailer at the right.

In 1969, a new kind of experimental enclosure was constructed as a prototypical test-object (Fig. 1). A cylindrical form was selected for several reasons, such as the simplification of construction and air distribution and the better applicability to the enclosure of fruit trees. The greater innovation was the absence of a closure on top of the chamber. This appeared to be the logical answer to the entrapment of heat and the lack of precipitation and pollinating insects in the chamber. In the summer of 1970, two such chambers were tested in the field and the results of these tests have been published (Mandl, Weinstein, McCune & Keveny, 1973) concurrently with those that described the construction and performance of a different kind of open-top, field chamber (Heagle, Body & Heck, 1973).

During the years that have passed since the chambers were first built and tested at Yonkers, their numbers and uses have increased in field experiments. The results and goals of this and other experimentation can serve as illustrations of the performance of the chamber as well as the criteria by which its performance was measured in studies of the effects of airborne fluoride and photochemical oxidants.

Approximation to ambient conditions·

One reason for field experimentation is that if plants are ordinarily affected by pollutants in the field, then experimentation will be more relevant or realistically informative when performed under field conditions. One common observation is that plants grown in greenhouses or controlled-environment chambers do not have the same appearance or characteristics as those grown in the field unless special care or equipment is used. Because the tolerance of the plant for the pollutant is one characteristic that may be changed by a departure from the ambient environment, the exposure of field-grown plants enables the response of a plant to pollution to be investigated with a minimum of an effect on the response itself.

'Under field conditions' denotes not a single condition but many that are continuously changing. When a population of plants is treated under a range of environmental conditions the field trial can be used to ascertain not only the degree of effect but also the likelihood of any effect at all. It also affords the opportunity to study a range of phenotypes and for this reason mobility of the chambers is important. By moving the chamber to where the plants are growing, instead of growing plants in the chamber, one can assign treatments according to the characteristics or previous behaviour of the experiment units. It is possible that field experiments may serve not only to reduce bias but also to control error and to broaden the range of inference when the occurrence of a pollutant is to be related to its probable effect.

Although short-term experiments revealed no difference in growth or appearance between plants grown in the open and those enclosed by a chamber (with unfiltered air), it is still uncertain as to whether enclosure alters the growth and development of plants over an entire growing season. Environmental conditions, such as temperature, precipitation, the occurrence of pollinating insects and concentration of oxidant, more closely approximate those of the ambient environment than in the completely enclosed chambers used previously. It should be added that as the occurrence of a sudden failure of electrical power has become all too probable, the decreased entrapment of heat has become a more and more desirable feature. However, it is possible that the walls of the chamber and the air handling system, which isolate the internal atmospheric environment of the chamber from the ambient, may affect the plants. Fibreglass walls alter, to some degree, the amount of distribution of solar radiation. But T. Keller & J. Bucher (personal communication) in seeking to mitigate this by the substitution of a clear acrylic plastic for the fibreglass panels, found that the former could focus sunlight in the chamber and thereby burn foliage. The air distribution system reduces the formation of dew and may also alter gaseous exchange. Experiments over the past three years, in which comparisons of enclosed and unenclosed plants could be made, have used vegetable crops to study the effects of ambient oxidants on yield. In one year, the yield of tomato fruit (measured by weight) was greater in unenclosed plots. But in subsequent years, predation by wildlife on the unenclosed plants has vitiated any further comparisons.

Contamination by ambient air

The intrusion of ambient air through the top of the chamber has continued to be a subject of interest for several reasons. When the effects of ambient pollutants are studied, it increases their concentration within the chamber. When the effects of hydrogen fluoride are studied, ambient air may dilute its concentration, alter its distribution and produce an interactive effect with it that is inseparable from the effect of hydrogen fluoride itself. With the use of a mesh covering to reduce ambient intrusion, measurements outside and inside a chamber (receiving charcoal-filtered air) over a 9-day period had previously shown that the concentration of oxidant within the chamber was about 30% that of the ambient (Mandl et al., 1973). Because no detectable oxidant passed the filter assembly, this concentration of oxidant represented the degree of contamination by ambient intrusion.

Further information on this problem has been accumulated in more extensive measurements during the past two years. Oxidant concentrations were measured inside and outside a chamber receiving filtered air for 99 days during the summer of 1973 (D. C. MacLean & R. E. Schneider, unpublished results). On the whole, the concentration of oxidants within the chamber ranged from 30 to 40% of the ambient. However, a tabulation of oxidant concentrations and meteorological conditions over a period of three years by Jacobson & Salottolo (1975) indicated that the concentration of oxidants at Yonkers tended to be lower under the conditions of wind velocity that increased the intrusion of ambient air. Thus, estimates of ambient exclusion may depend upon the meteorological relationships between site, source and pollutant, and greater or lesser degrees of contamination may be found by others.

The modular construction of the chamber does allow an increase in the height of the walls (from 2.4 to 3.6 m) by the addition of a third section. This would tend to decrease ambient intrusion in the vicinity of the plant's foliage. On the other hand, complete exclusion of an ambient pollutant may not be necessary for some experiments. A tabulation of the hourly means by MacLean & Schneider during the summer of 1973 at Yonkers (unpublished observations) showed that the US air quality standard for oxidants was exceeded 11% of the time in an unfiltered chamber but for only 1 hour in the filtered chamber. The yields of beans and tomatoes were 25 and 30% higher, respectively, in the filtered air compared to unfiltered air. Thus, studies of ambient pollutants by means of the open-top chamber afford an estimate of what agricultural benefits could accrue, were a reduction in pollution of a certain degree to occur.

Uniformity of pollutant distribution

The uniformity of a pollutant's distribution is important for the obvious reason that one would like to have the greater mass of foliage on a tree or crop in the chamber exposed to the same dose. Even if the concentration of pollutant is not uniform, one would like to have its distribution a stable characteristic so that a minimal number of sampling points is required for routine monitoring in order to characterise accurately the dosage given.

Dynamic sampling methods for ozone (O_3), sulphur dioxide (SO_2), and hydrogen fluoride showed that the concentrations of injected pollutants were as uniform as in any previously used field chamber (relative standard deviations of 7 to 15%). But static sampling methods for hydrogen fluoride (limed candles) showed that the flux of pollutant varied considerably from point to point within the chamber. This static sampling method is sensitive to the rate of air flow as well as concentration of hydrogen fluoride. Thus, the equalisation of the flux of fluoride within the chamber would not only provide more uniform doses of hydrogen fluoride but also tend to reduce the variability in the growth and response of plants that could be caused by differences in stomatal function, gaseous exchange and water relationships.

The distribution of air and pollutant within the chamber is determined by the configuration of both the chamber and the air distribution system or plenum. In previous tests (Mandl et al., 1973), the plenum was a circular tube that ran along the interior surface of the chamber at its base. A single line of regularly spaced holes in the plenum discharged air towards the centre of the chamber in a horizontal plane. Further tests for uniformity in the vertical and horizontal distribution of fluoride have used both dynamic and static sampling methods. The latter consisted of lime impregnated cylinders of filter paper (Mandl et al., 1973), with two such cylinders orientated axially along each of three orthogonal axes (one vertical, two horizontal) at each sampling point in the chamber.

Although different locations and patterns of perforation of the plenum
were tested, the greatest improvement to date in the distribution of fluoride
was achieved merely by a rotation of the plenum that changed the direction
of the air discharged from it. One effect of the orientation of the plenum is
illustrated in Fig. 2, where the vertical distribution or profile was obtained
with the static collectors. Within the lower 1.2 m of the chamber, the most
uniform vertical distribution was obtained when air was discharged at an
angle of 45° to the horizontal. This orientation, which provided more complete mixing, has been used for experiments with fruit trees where the foliar
mass is centred in the chamber and located more than 1 m above the ground.

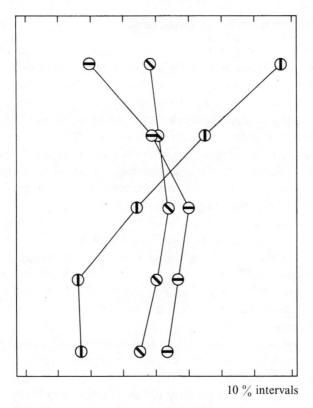

10 % intervals

Direction of air discharge from plenum:
⊖ horizontal; ⊕ vertical; ⊘ at 45°.

Fig. 2.   Effect of plenum orientation on the vertical distribution of
hydrogen fluoride in the open-top chamber. Static samplers were located
at distances from the bottom of the chamber (vertical axis) of 0, 30, 60, 90,
and 120 cm. Distances along the horizontal axis, marked at intervals of
10%, indicate negative (to the left) and positive (to the right) differences
from the overall mean for each orientation of the plenum.

When the chamber was used for crops with a lower canopy, such as alfalfa, grasses or beans, the plenum was rotated to discharge air vertically along the walls of the chamber. Although the vertical profile produced by this orientation of the plenum is not so uniform as the others (Fig. 2), it may be similar to what would be found above a crop in the field. This orientation avoided a direct flow of air on to the foliage and resulted in a more uniform horizontal distribution of fluoride in the space of the lower third of the chamber. In three different tests, thirty-six static monitors were distributed in horizontal planes, 30 and 60 cm above the floor of the chamber, along radii 60° apart, at points 30, 60 and 90 cm from the centre of the chamber. When air was discharged at 45°, 30% of the values were within 10% of the overall mean, 26% between 10 and 20%, 30% between 20 to 40%, and about 9% were more than 65% from the mean. On the other hand when air was discharged vertically, 30% of the values were within 5% of the overall mean, 32% were between 5 and 10%, 31% were between 10 and 20%, and 7% were between 20 and 32% of the mean.

In the many tests of the distribution of fluoride it was apparent that the air within the chambers moved in a pattern that was more similar to the cyclical flow of a convection cell than the laminar flow of a wind tunnel. The results described above with static sampling methods were conducted without plants in the chamber and therefore do not reflect the effects of sinks on the operational distribution of fluoride. However, they do indicate some characteristics of the mass of air and pollutants that move into the spaces occupied by foliage. Probably, the system most in need of improvement is that of the distribution of air, and it is hoped that such will be forthcoming with increased use of this kind of chamber.

Simulation of realistic exposures

A goal of experimentation with the open-top chamber continues to be the simulation of realistic exposures. The comparison of plants grown in chambers receiving filtered or unfiltered air where ambient pollutants are present is one approach. Another has been to add a pollutant to the air received by some chambers each 24-hour period at a concentration equal to that which was found in the preceding 24 hours (Thompson et al., 1967). The reproduction of specific, actual, ambient concentrations is a powerful means for the investigation of the responses of plants to a pollutant at a certain site. However, it is difficult to generalise to other exposures or other sites until the results of many trials have been accumulated.

A more common approach has been to identify the significant characteristics of exposures that are known to occur and then to determine the effects of systematic changes in those characteristics. Until recent years, there have not been many data available indicating concentrations of gaseous fluoride around sources in North America, especially for averaging or sampling periods of 24 hours or less. One technological obstacle to the gaining of this information has been the lack of air monitoring methods that could discriminate between gaseous and particulate forms of airborne fluoride, operate reliably when unattended in the field, and prove sufficiently economic in their initial and operational costs.

The combination of a citric-acid-treated filter for the collection of particulate fluoride with a bicarbonate-coated tube for the collection of gaseous fluoride, resulted in a new air monitoring system that could discriminate between these two forms of airborne fluoride (Weinstein & Mandl, 1971). The development of the dual paper tape sampler produced an apparatus that performed the same function but with even shorter sampling periods for the monitoring of ambient or experimentally produced fluoride-containing atmospheres (Weinstein & Mandl, 1971). Both methods have been used and compared in routine environmental monitoring programmes in the field and their results are in good agreement (Israel, 1974). With the accumulation of the results of such programmes (where data no longer needed to be expressed as a long-term mean), it was possible to determine some characteristics of realistic exposures and test the capacity of the field chamber to simulate them.

Occurrence of airborne fluoride

The frequency distribution is one means for the description of ambient concentrations of atmospheric fluoride (Schneider, 1968) and the frequency histograms shown in Fig. 3 are derived from simultaneous measurements made at five different sites around the same source. Each distribution is based upon more than 300 12-hour measurements of gaseous fluoride at each site for a 5-month period during the growing season.

One common feature of these distributions and others is that infrequent peaks or outliers at higher concentrations appear to be superimposed on a numerically preponderant distribution at much lower concentrations. It is obvious that distributions differ not only in location, estimated by mean or median, but also in dispersion or variance and degree of skewness. This last characteristic can become a dominant one when zero values occur frequently, as for example, Davison, Rand & Betts (1973) found for fluoride concentrations in rural areas. But even in the vicinity of an alumina reduction smelter, zero values were found 10, 31 and 37% of the time at three different air monitoring sites. Thus the mean may indicate the proportion of time that

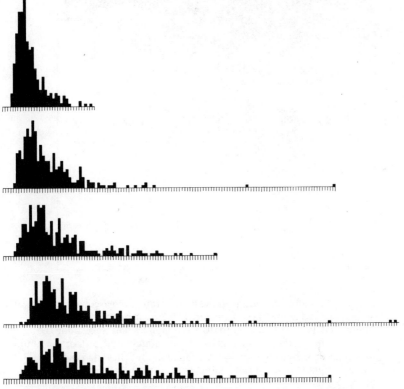

Fig. 3. Frequency distribution histograms for measurements of gaseous fluoride at five different sites around the same source. The data for each site are based on 12-hour samples over a period of 5 months. Intervals on the horizontal axis are 0.01 μg F m^{-3} and the vertical axis is the frequency of occurrence.

any detectable concentration of fluoride is present and the atmospheric concentrations of hydrogen fluoride may be more comparable to the Poisson than to the normal distribution.

It should also be noted that these distributions are composites: they reflect the operations of the source, the intervention of local meteorological conditions and the distribution of sampling and analytical error. Thus the tendency of values to occur in periodic clusters at low concentrations may represent fractional scale divisions and rounding errors in the analytical system when the same volumes of air are sampled. Zeros may represent those values below the limit of analytical detection.

Nevertheless, a considerable proportion of zero values, plus the knowledge that winds are not persistent or constant, indicate that exposures to fluoride are not continuous at any one site. Thus, it is also necessary to characterise

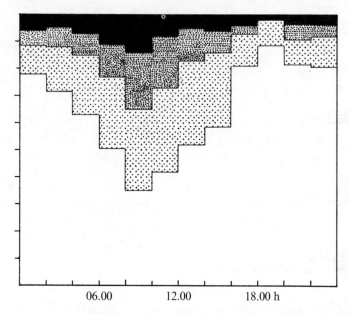

Fig. 4. Quotidian variations in the concentration of gaseous fluoride near an alumina reduction plant. Data for each 2-hour period of the day (horizontal axis) represent more than 190 samples. Distance along the vertical scale, marked in intervals of 10%, is equal to the proportion of time, that concentrations (μg F m^{-3}) were found in the following ranges: white, 0; light stipple, >0 and ≤ 0.1; heavy stipple, >0.1 and ≤ 1.0; black, >1.0.

the occurrence of airborne fluoride by the temporal distribution of events. The tabulation of more than 2300 2-hour samples of gaseous fluoride at a single site near an alumina reduction plant gives the distribution shown in Fig. 4. There is a definite cycle in the distribution of airborne fluoride that reflects the quotidian changes in meteorological conditions. It would seem likely that where fluoride-containing emissions are distributed by on- and off-shore winds or up- and down-canyon flows of air, similar patterns of exposure may be expected.

These air monitoring data indicate that the field exposure system should have the following characteristics. Firstly, the concentration of hydrogen fluoride should be maintained within rather narrow limits in continuous operation so that portions of the basic frequency distribution can be isolated and studied for their effect. Secondly, the system must be able to deliver a predetermined amount of hydrogen fluoride without preliminary operation so that single exposures to the outliers or peaks can be simulated. Thirdly, if quotidian cycles are to be simulated, the entire system should reach the desired concentration and return to baseline or background rapidly.

Responses of plants to airborne fluoride

It was also important that a knowledge of the nature of the plant's response to hydrogen fluoride be used in determining the desirable characteristics of our field exposure system and its use. The relation between dose and response depends upon many factors, such as species or cultivar, stage of development, environmental conditions and the particular response or measure of it that is used (NAS, 1971). Some investigators (Treshow & Harner, 1968) have found that the relationship between concentration of hydrogen fluoride and some measure of growth, such as an increase in mass or height, is not a simple one. That is, one concentration of hydrogen fluoride would result in an increased growth but a higher one would result in decreased growth or be without any significant effect. It is possible that if a response were studied continually throughout an exposure, some better understanding would be obtained of its relationship to the concentration, and to changes in the concentration, of hydrogen fluoride.

One of the persistent problems in the interpretation of a dose–response relationship, especially with an accumulated pollutant such as hydrogen fluoride, is whether one exposure is equivalent to another if both result in the same mean concentration. In one series of experiments, milo maize (*Sorghum* sp. vc. Northrup King 222A) was exposed to hydrogen fluoride over a 9-day period (D. C. MacLean & R. E. Schneider, unpublished results). Two concentrations, 1.6 or 3.3 μg F m^{-3}, were used and by transferring groups of plants from one concentration to another every 3 days, eight different patterns of exposure were created.

Measurements of yield at maturity showed that plants exposed to the lower concentration throughout the exposure produced more seeds than control plants, and that the number of seeds decreased progressively as plants were given one or two periods at the higher concentration. On the other hand, if the data were analysed as a factorial experiment, increases in concentration of hydrogen fluoride during the middle or last 3-day periods decreased the yield of seed and acted independently. An increase in concentration during the first 3-day period did not affect yield but significantly affected the response of plants to a subsequent change in concentration: an increase in concentration during the middle period was more effective when plants were previously exposed to 1.6 than to 3.3 μg F m^{-3}. Thus the effect of a change in concentration of hydrogen fluoride depended on the concentration of hydrogen fluoride in a previous or subsequent exposure.

Although the assumption of a linear additive model to describe the effects of a change in dose should still be questioned, further information on the response of plants to the dose and pattern of hydrogen fluoride exposure came from measurements of the carbon dioxide exchange of field plots (D. C. McCune, L. H. Weinstein & J. Mancini, unpublished results). Scheduled treatments of 0, 0.7, 2.2 and 4.8 μg F m^{-3} were assigned to sixteen plots of milo maize cv. Martin's in a Latin Square design. Samples of ambient air and the exhaust from chambers that completely enclosed the plots were taken simultaneously for the analysis of carbon dioxide before, during, and after a 14-day exposure period. The results of measurements of carbon dioxide uptake are shown in Fig. 5 where the effects of the different hydrogen fluoride treatments are plotted day by day with reference to the controls.

The plots exposed to the lowest concentration of hydrogen fluoride

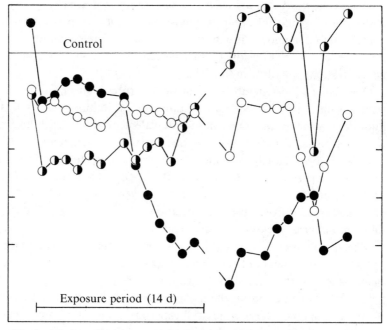

Fig. 5.   Carbon dioxide uptake by plots of milo maize (*Sorghum* sp. cv. Martin's) before, during, and after a 14-day exposure to hydrogen fluoride. Exposure period is indicated along the horizontal axis. Four measurements per plot were taken between 09.00 and 15.00 h EST each day and each point is the daily mean of four plots receiving the following mean concentrations of hydrogen fluoride (μg F m^{-3}): ○, 0.7; ◑, 2.2 for 12d then 1.7 for 2d; ●, 3.5 for first 7d and then >5 for 7d. Horizontal line indicates control and distances along the vertical axis are marked at intervals of one standard error of the mean, based on between-plot variance for one day. (Standard errors of the mean between days for the same treatment are less than one-quarter as great.)

(0.7 μg F m^{-3}) tended to maintain their original rate of carbon dioxide uptake (although lower than the mean of plots chosen as controls) throughout the exposure and post-exposure periods. Heat and water stress occurred during the latter part of the post-exposure period and both treated and control plants showed wilting and necrotic lesions owing to this condition. In contrast, plots exposed to the middle and highest concentrations of hydrogen fluoride showed a decrease in the rate of carbon dioxide uptake after 1 day of exposure, and this depression continued without any great change until the concentration of hydrogen fluoride was changed.

In plots receiving the middle concentration of hydrogen fluoride, a change from 2.2 to 1.7 μg F m^{-3} occurred 2 days before exposure ceased and was associated with an increase in the rate of carbon dioxide uptake. The complete cessation of exposure resulted in a greater rate of carbon dioxide uptake than the controls. In plots exposed to the highest concentration of hydrogen fluoride, an abrupt increase in the mean concentrations from 3.5 to those greater than 5 μg F m^{-3} after 7 days of exposure resulted in a precipitous drop in the rate of carbon dioxide uptake, and the subsequent appearance of necrotic and chlorotic lesions that are induced by hydrogen fluoride in this species of plant. In general, changes in carbon dioxide uptake by milo maize represented a response to hydrogen fluoride that was relatively rapid, time-dependent and sensitive to changes in hydrogen fluoride concentration or cessation of exposure.

The results of these two experiments with milo maize further demonstrate that a field exposure system should provide stable and reproducible concentrations of hydrogen fluoride, whether used for continuous or intermittent, long-term and low-level exposures, or for short-term peaks. When a series of concentrations is used to determine the nature of the dose–response relationship, stability not only ensures that the doses will be discrete but minimises the confounding effects of changes in concentration during the exposure. When intermittent exposures are used, reproducibility aids in determining the difference between them and continuous exposures as well as what conditions must be met so that separate exposures appear to act independently.

Performance of the field exposure system

The capacity of the open-top chamber and hydrogen fluoride generator to provide continuous or periodic exposures, especially at lower concentrations of hydrogen fluoride, was investigated in field tests. Two chambers provided continuous concentrations of hydrogen fluoride over a 2-month period. The mean concentrations found were 0.50 and 0.25 μg F m^{-3} with standard deviations of 0.08 and 0.03 μg F m^{-3}, respectively. In another field test, hydrogen fluoride was injected from 09.00 to 15.00 h EST on alternate days. A paper tape sampler, set for a 2-hour cycle, monitored the concentration of hydrogen fluoride within the chamber at a point in the centre about 1 m above the ground (about 30 cm below the foliar mass of three dwarf peach trees enclosed by the chamber).

The results are illustrated in Fig. 6 and show that within 2 hours after injection of hydrogen fluoride started, the concentration reached 50% of its peak value of $1 \mu g \, F \, m^{-3}$. After injection ceased, the concentration

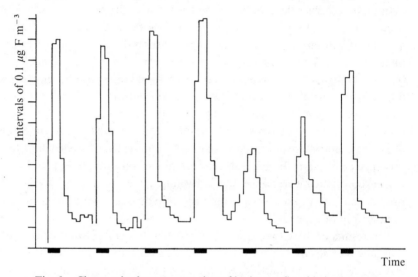

Fig. 6.   Changes in the concentration of hydrogen fluoride in the open-top field chamber produced by periodic injection of the gas. Vertical axis shows concentration in each 2-hour sample with intervals of $0.1 \mu g \, F \, m^{-3}$ marked. Horizontal axis represents time, with periods of hydrogen fluoride injection indicated by bars. The lower concentrations of the fourth and fifth cycles show the effect of precipitation during these periods.

dropped by about 50% in 2 hours and then slowly decayed to a base level of about $0.2 \mu g \, F \, m^{-3}$. The achievement of replicate peak concentrations was rather good in four successive periods. However, the obvious difference between these and the next two periods shows the effect of precipitation: the lower and broader peaks are probably due to the effect of free water on surfaces of the chamber, plenum and foliage. In other field chambers and in controlled-environment chambers the presence of free water and sorptive surfaces also tended to smooth or attenuate changes in the concentration of hydrogen fluoride.

It was apparent that this field exposure system could not achieve the complete degree of control over hydrogen fluoride concentration that was desired for the simulation of periodic, diurnal or nocturnal exposures. Indeed, the only way a short-term peak could be achieved was by removal of the chamber immediately after the injection of hydrogen fluoride had ceased. Nevertheless, it is possible to study the effects of peak height and frequency if one also allows for some means of determining the additional or interactive effect of the baseline concentration.

Much better control over short-term exposures has been achieved with ozone and sulphur dioxide in field fumigations. Consequently, the performance of the open-top chamber may be more suitable for these pollutants, which are of more general interest than hydrogen fluoride. On the other hand, the greatest use of open-top chambers may be for determining the effects of ambient atmospheric pollution.

In this application, the major advances in field experimentation may come through the development of techniques that can selectively exclude certain compounds from the chamber, because phytotoxic pollutants seldom occur singly. Whether open-top chambers are chosen for studies of introduced or excluded pollutants, their wider use will certainly lead to improvements in them and in knowledge that can be applied to the problem of environmental quality.

References

Davison, A. W., Rand, A. W. & Betts, W. E. (1973). Measurement of atmospheric fluoride concentrations in urban areas. *Environmental Pollution* **5**, 23–33.

Heagle, A. S., Body, D. E. & Heck, W. W. (1973). An open-top field chamber to assess the impact of air pollution on plants. *Journal of Environmental Quality* **2**, 365–8.

Israel, G. (1974). Evaluation and comparison of three atmospheric fluoride monitors under field conditions. *Atmospheric Environment* **8**, 159–66.

Jacobson, J. S. & Salottolo, G. D. (1975). Photochemical oxidants in the New York–New Jersey metropolitan area. *Atmospheric Environment* **9**, 321–32.

Mandl, R. H., Weinstein, L. H., McCune, D. C. & Keveny, M. (1973). A cylindrical, open-top chamber for the exposure of plants to air pollutants in the field. *Journal of Environmental Quality* **2**, 371–6.

NAS (1971). *Biologic effects of atmospheric pollutants: fluorides.* National Academy of Sciences, Washington, DC.

Schneider, W. (1968). Daueruntersuchungen zur Fluorproblem in einem industriellen Ballungsgebiet. *Staub-Reinhaltung der Luft* **28**, 13–18.

Thompson, C. R., Taylor, O. C., Thomas, M. D. & Ivie, J. O. (1967). Effects of air pollutants on apparent photosynthesis and water use by citrus trees. *Environmental Science & Technology* **1**, 644–50.

Treshow, M. & Harner, F. M. (1968). Growth responses of pinto bean and alfalfa to sublethal fluoride concentrations. *Canadian Journal of Botany* **46**, 1207–10.

Weinstein, L. H. & Mandl, R. H. (1971). The separation and collection of gaseous and particulate fluorides. *Verein Deutscher Ingenieure Berichte* **164**, 53–70.

W.J.MANNING & W.A.FEDER

Effects of ozone on economic plants

Introduction

Ozone (O_3) is the most common gaseous phytotoxic air pollutant in the north-eastern United States. Concentrations of ozone ranging from 4 to 9 parts per hundred million (pphm) frequently occur during the growing season. This ozone results primarily from a complex, photochemically induced reaction between the hydrocarbons and nitrogen oxides of motor vehicle exhaust. The nitrogen oxides produce atomic oxygen which combines with oxygen in the air to form ozone (Stern, 1962). Depending upon air movements and atmospheric conditions, the ozone formed can travel long distances and injure susceptible plants over very wide areas (Heggestad & Heck, 1971).

Many cultivars of economic crop plants are known to be injured by ozone (Hill *et al.*, 1961; Feder, 1970, 1973; Jacobson & Hill, 1970; Gentile, Feder, Young & Santer, 1971; Heggestad & Heck, 1971; Manning, Feder & Vardaro, 1974; Manning & Vardaro, 1975). Commonly affected plants in the north-eastern USA include cultivars of bean, onion, potato, spinach, squash and tobacco. Injury characteristically appears first on the older leaves. Symptoms range from leaf yellowing to punctate white to bronze stippling to extensive necrotic flecking and blotching (Hill *et al.*, 1961; Hindawi, 1970; Jacobson & Hill, 1970; Heggestad & Heck, 1971). Cumulative injury results in premature senescence and enhanced maturity (Heggestad & Heck, 1971; Feder, 1973; Tomlinson & Rich, 1973; Manning *et al.*, 1974).

While it is well-known that ozone can injure many plants, the significance of this injury in terms of plant growth, development and yield has not been clearly and completely determined for any given plant. Technical problems make it difficult to compare the growth of plants grown in ozone-influenced and ozone-free environments. This is particularly true in experiments conducted under natural field conditions. Results of a number of attempts to determine the effects of ozone on plant yields have been summarised elsewhere (Feder, 1970, 1973; Manning *et al.*, 1974). The results of some of our recent greenhouse and field investigations on the cumulative effects of ozone on the growth, development and yield of bean and tomato plants are presented here.

48   W. J. MANNING AND W. A. FEDER

Materials and methods

Greenhouse experiments

All greenhouse experiments were conducted in four identical polyethylene-covered greenhouses, each $8 \times 4 \times 3$ m. Motor-driven blowers were used to introduce all incoming air through ducts containing activated charcoal filters to remove ozone and other oxidants. Ozone was selectively generated within the greenhouses as desired. Welsbach ozone generators were used and concentrations were determined with continuously operating Mast meters equipped with sulphur dioxide scrubbers. Mast meters were also used to monitor ozone under field conditions.

The dwarf tomato (*Lycopersicon esculentum* Mill.) cultivar Tiny Tim and the standard cultivar Bonny Best were used. A number of bush and climbing bean cultivars (*Phaseolus vulgaris* L.) were also examined for ozone sensitivity under greenhouse conditions.

All plants were grown from seed in the greenhouses under the conditions of the particular experiment. Potting compost consisted of a steamed mixture of $\frac{1}{3}$ peat $+\frac{2}{3}$ Merrimac fine sandy loam. Unless otherwise noted, plants were exposed to ozone for 8 h per day, 5 d per week.

Field experiments

All bean plants were grown in single 2.8-m rows in a field of Merrimac fine sandy loam. Each row contained twenty plants. Four replications were used. Where bean plants were treated with the systemic fungicide benomyl (methyl-1-(butylcarbamoyl)-2-benzimidazole carbamate), each replication contained two 2.8-m rows of each bean cultivar, one sprayed and one non-sprayed.

Where data were analysed statistically, either the standard analysis of variance or Duncan's multiple range test was used.

Experimentation and results

Greenhouse experiments

Growth and development of tomato plants   Tomato plants are known to be sensitive to ozone and cultivars vary in sensitivity (Gentile *et al.*, 1971). Tiny Tim tomato is very sensitive to ozone and completes its life cycle in a short span of time, which makes it a good experimental plant. Bonny Best, a standard cultivar, is less sensitive to ozone and grows vigorously. In one experiment, plants of both cultivars were grown for 45 days in either ozone-free air or ozone at 8–10 pphm. Five replications of ten plants each were used for each cultivar in each air regime. Measurements of plant height were made 25, 35 and 45 days after initiation of the experiment. At termination, internodes 1 through 4 were measured and dry weights of tops were determined. In a related experiment, Tiny Tim plants were grown under the same conditions for 60 days. Five replications of three plants each were used. Root dry weights were determined at termination.

Table 1. *Influence of long-term low levels of ozone (8–10 pphm) on height of tomato plants*

Cultivars and treatments	Plant heights* (cm) by days after start of experiment		
	25	35	45
Tiny Tim			
Ozone	3.9 x†	4.9 x	8.6 x
No ozone	5.3 y	8.2 y	14.2 y
Bonny Best			
Ozone	10.4 x	13.8 x	21.3 x
No ozone	11.8 x	14.6 x	22.5 x

* Average per five replications, ten plants each.

† Values not followed by the same letters are significantly different ($P = 0.01$), using Duncan's multiple range test.

Table 2. *Influence of long-term low levels of ozone (8–10 pphm) on internode lengths of tomato plants*

Cultivars and treatments	Internode lengths* (cm) 45 days after start of experiment			
	1	2	3	4
Tiny Tim				
Ozone	0.58 x†	0.72 x	0.90 x	1.05 x
No ozone	1.05 y	1.41 y	2.02 y	2.57 y
Bonny Best				
Ozone	1.86 x	2.17 x	2.49 x	3.70 x
No ozone	2.30 x	2.54 x	2.94 x	3.72 x

* Average per five replications, ten plants each.

† Values not followed by the same letters are significantly different ($P = 0.01$), using Duncan's multiple range test.

Moderate foliar injury on Tiny Tim and slight to moderate injury on Bonny Best was observed on cotyledons and successive older leaves of plants exposed to ozone. For Tiny Tim ozone significantly ($P = 0.01$) decreased plant heights 25, 35 and 45 days after initiation of the experiment (Table 1), length of internodes 1 through 4 (Table 2), dry weights of plant tops (Table 3) and root dry weights (Table 4). In Bonny Best the decreases observed were not

Table 3.   *Influence of long-term low levels of ozone (8–10 pphm) on dry weight of tops of tomato plants*

Cultivars	Dry weights* of tops (g) 45 days after start of experiment	
	Ozone	No ozone
Tiny Tim	0.63 x†	1.28 y
Bonny Best	1.68 x	2.10 x

* Average per five replications, ten plants each.

† Values not followed by the same letters are significantly different ($P = 0.01$), using Duncan's multiple range test.

Table 4.   *Influence of long-term low levels of ozone (8–10 pphm) on dry weights of roots of tomato plants*

Cultivar	Dry weights* of roots (g) 60 days after start of experiment	
	Ozone	No ozone
Tiny Tim	5.1 x†	13.6 y

* Average per five replications, three plants each.

† Values not followed by the same letters are significantly different ($P = 0.01$), using Duncan's multiple range test.

significant. The depressant effects of ozone on growth and development of Tiny Tim tomato can also be observed by comparing Figs. 1 and 2.

Yield of tomato plants   In an initial experiment, Tiny Tim tomato plants were grown for 60 days in either ozone-free air or ozone at 8–10 pphm, 5 h per day, 5 d per week. Five replications of three plants each were used. At

termination, the total number of fruit set and their fresh weight were determined. Ozone significantly and drastically reduced the average number of
fruit set per plant and their weight (Table 5).

Table 5.   *Influence of long-term low levels of
ozone (8–10 pphm) on total number and weight
of Tiny Tim tomato fruit*

	Yields* 60 days after start of experiment	
Treatments	Number of fruit	Weight of fruit (g)
Ozone	11.4 y	22.7 y
No ozone	79.1 x†	255.3 x

* Average per five replications, three plants each.

† Values not followed by the same letters are significantly
different ($P = 0.01$), using Duncan's multiple range test.

A more extensive experiment was conducted to examine more closely the
depressant effect of ozone on yields of Tiny Tim tomato. Uniform plants,
with developing flower clusters, were selected for study. These plants had
been grown from seed in ozone-free air, ozone at 8–10 pphm for 5 h per day,
5 d per week (steady ozone), or ozone at 5 pphm for 2 h followed by 8–10
pphm ozone for 3 h, 5 d per week (uneven ozone). The first five flower clusters
(labelled A through E, with A the oldest and E the youngest) were tagged and
the appearance of buds, flowers, and fruit were carefully observed. All plants

Table 6.   *Influence of ozone on fruit set by Tiny Tim tomato flower
clusters in different stages of development*

Cluster designations (oldest to youngest)*	No. days required for 10 fruit to set per cluster		
	No ozone	Uneven ozone†	Steady ozone‡
A	7	21	None set
B	7	17	35
C	7	14	21
D	8	16	17
E	9	15	16

* First five clusters formed. Average per ten plants.

† 2 h at 5 pphm ozone and 3 h at 8–10 pphm ozone per day.

‡ Ozone at 8–10 pphm, 5 h per day.

Fig. 1.   Tiny Tim tomato plant grown in charcoal-filtered, ozone-free air.
Note developing fruit and vigorous habit.

Fig. 2. Tiny Tim tomato plant exposed to ozone (8–10 pphm, 5 h per day, 5 d per week for 9 weeks). Note smaller plant size and absence of developing fruit compared with Fig. 1.

were maintained for 9 weeks in the same air regime in which they had been grown.

Both uneven and steady ozone were found to greatly increase the number of days required for the tagged flower clusters to set ten fruits each (Table 6). The effect was most pronounced with steady ozone and with the oldest

Table 7. *Influence of ozone on Tiny Tim tomato flower buds, flowers, and fruit set by the first five clusters*

Ratios	% flower or fruit development by ozone treatments		
	No ozone	Uneven ozone*	Steady ozone†
Buds:flowers	96‡	95	87
Flowers:fruit set	95	78	56
Fruit set:total yield	64	51	47

* 2 h at 5 pphm ozone and 3 h at 8–10 pphm ozone per day.

† Ozone at 8–10 pphm, 5 h per day.

‡ Average per ten plants.

clusters (A and B). This depressant effect on the rate of fruit set can also be seen by comparing Figs 1 and 2. Ratios of the number of buds formed to flowers set, number of flowers to fruit set, and number of fruit set to final number of fruit harvested, were calculated and expressed as percentages (Table 7). Steady ozone somewhat reduced the number of flowers set for buds formed. Both uneven and steady ozone drastically reduced the percentages of fruit set compared to the number of flowers. Reductions were also

Table 8. *Influence of ozone on Tiny Tim tomato fruit yield by size and maturity: first five clusters*

Treatments	Fruit yield by sizes‡			
	Small	Medium	Large	Totals
No ozone	97	50	24 (12 ripe)	171
Uneven ozone*	84	58 (2 ripe)	11 (1 ripe)	153
Steady ozone†	41	4	3	48

* 2 h at 5 pphm ozone followed by 3 h at 8–10 pphm ozone per day for 9 weeks.

† Ozone at 8–10 pphm, 5 h per day for 9 weeks.

‡ Average per ten plants.

Fig. 3. Comparative yield of tomato fruit from first five clusters of Tiny Tim plants exposed to ozone for 9 weeks. H-1S, no ozone; H-2S, 8–10 pphm ozone (steady ozone); H-3S, 2 h ozone at 5 pphm, followed by 3 h at 8–10 pphm (uneven ozone). Row in foreground represents small-sized fruit, second row medium-sized fruit and third row large-sized fruit. (See also Table 8.)

noted for the percentages of fruit harvested compared to the number of fruit initially set. Fruit were harvested at termination and were graded for relative size (small, medium, and large) and ripeness (Table 8). Steady ozone reduced fruit numbers in all size categories and also the total yield. The number of large fruit was reduced by uneven ozone. The number of large and ripe fruit was greatest in the no ozone treatment. This can also be seen in Fig. 3.

Sensitivity of bean cultivars to ozone Beans are known to be sensitive to ozone injury (Howell, 1972; Evans, 1973; Davis & Kress, 1974; Manning & Vardaro, 1975). To determine whether bean cultivars vary in sensitivity to ozone by flower colour, seed colour and plant habit, twenty-two commercial green pod bush bean cultivars and forty-four with trailing or climbing habit (including thirty Plant Introductory Lines from the Plant Introduction Station, Geneva, New York) were initially screened in the greenhouse for ozone sensitivity at 3–5 and 8–10 pphm ozone, 8 h per day, 5 d per week, for

30 days. Five replications of three plants each were used for each air regime. Cultivars were evaluated for ozone sensitivity by assigning them to injury classes from 1 to 6, where 1 = no visible foliar injury, 2 = 15% injury, 3 = 30% injury, 4 = 45% injury, 5 = 60% injury and 6 = 75% injury and greater.

At 3–5 pphm ozone, only the ozone-sensitive bush bean cultivar Tempo (white flowers) (Howell, 1972) exhibited injury in class 5. At 8–10 pphm, all cultivars showed injury in classes 4, 5 and 6, except the bush bean cultivars Richgreen and Tendergreen (white flowers) in class 2.

Field experiments

Suppression of ozone injury by benomyl   Air pollution is thought to affect plants in the field by promoting early senescence or growth reductions which may be reflected in lower yields (Landau & Brandt, 1970). Due to technical difficulties in comparing plant growth and yield under field conditions in the presence or absence of air pollutants such as ozone, little quantitative information is available (Manning *et al.*, 1974). For this reason we grew the ozone-sensitive and the ozone-resistant green pod bush bean cultivars Tempo and Tenderwhite (Howell, 1972) in a field experiment. Half of the plants were sprayed once a week with benomyl at 2.4 g l^{-1}, beginning 5 days after seedling emergence and continuing until all pods had been removed for evaluation. Benomyl is known to suppress oxidant injury on beans, probably by inhibiting ozone-induced senescence (Tomlinson & Rich, 1973; Manning & Vardaro, 1974). Pods were picked once a week for 5 weeks. All pods 12 cm or greater in length (edible size) were removed at each harvest. Pods were counted and fresh weights determined. Results were compared within cultivars, but not between them as they differ enough in characters as to make such comparisons unrealistic. Two continuously operating Mast meters were used to determine ozone concentrations.

Ozone concentrations were high enough and persistent (335 hourly average readings of 4 pphm and higher) throughout the experiment to cause yellowing, bronzing and premature senescence of Tempo leaves, all of which are symptoms of chronic ozone injury (Heggestad & Heck, 1971; Howell, 1972). Only occasional scattered symptoms occurred on a few leaves of Tenderwhite. Foliar sprays of benomyl reduced symptoms and premature senescence of Tempo leaves by 75–80%. Slight injury on Tenderwhite was not suppressed by benomyl. Benomyl did not alter the incidence of parasitic diseases or insects. Non-sprayed plants of both cultivars bloomed earlier and bore pods earlier than sprayed plants. This is reflected in yield figures for week 1 (Table 9). Significantly greater numbers and weights of pods were obtained from sprayed Tempo plants at harvests 2 and 5 and for total yield. Significant differences

Table 9. *Benomyl foliar sprays: effects on yields of green pod bean cultivars sensitive to ozone injury (Tempo) and resistant to ozone injury (Tenderwhite)*

Cultivars and treatments	Average yields by weeks[d]					Average total yields
	1	2	3	4	5	
Tempo[a]						
No. of pods:						
sprayed[b]	77.3	213.2*	504.3	326.3	226.8**	1347.9**
non-sprayed	91.0	151.7*	417.3	234.0	127.3**	1021.3**
Wt of pods (g):						
sprayed	180.6	712.3*	1589.7	1225.1	1035.8*	4743.5**
non-sprayed	226.0	433.0*	1457.2	831.8	411.0*	3359.0**
Tenderwhite[c]						
No. of pods:						
sprayed	96.8	335.7	264.7	373.5	181.5	1252.2
non-sprayed	115.0	330.0	249.7	330.7	116.3	1141.7
Wt of pods (g):						
sprayed	354.3	1166.0	1011.6	1700.0	647.6	4879.5
non-sprayed	428.3	1529.5	977.6	1435.1	465.1	4835.6

[a] First harvest made 54 days after planting.

[b] Weekly foliar sprays of benomyl at 2.4 g l^{-1}.

[c] First harvest made 61 days after planting.

[d] Average per four replications, twenty plants each.

* Significantly different values ($P = 0.05$), standard analysis of variance.

** Significantly different values ($P = 0.01$), standard analysis of variance.

were not observed between any average yields from sprayed and non-sprayed plants of Tenderwhite.

Sensitivity of bean cultivars to ozone The same bean cultivars that were evaluated for ozone sensitivity in the greenhouse were grown in field plots from June through August to determine ozone sensitivity under natural conditions. The experiment was repeated three times. Injury classes used were the same as previously described.

Ozone concentrations (hourly averages) from 4 to 9 pphm were recorded for 335 hours during the experimental period. Except for cultivar Tempo (white flowers) with 60–75% injury, all other bush bean cultivars showed little or no injury. Most of these had white flowers. Susceptibility of climbing bean cultivars to ozone is summarised in Table 10. Twenty of the thirty white-flowered cultivars (66.6%), nine of the ten lavender-flowered cultivars (90%), and three of the four pink-flowered cultivars (75%) were sensitive to ozone, with injury ranging from 15–75%. Overall, thirty-two of the forty-four

Table 10.   *Susceptibility of climbing bean cultivars to ozone injury under field conditions*

Flower colours	No. of bean cultivars by ozone injury classes*						
	1	2	3	4	5	6	Totals
White	10	2	5	9	1	3	30
Pink	1	—	—	—	1	2	4
Lavender	1	3	2	1	2	1	10

* Average per four replications, twenty plants each. Two plantings, June–Sept., 1974.

1, no visible injury; 2, 15% injury; 3, 30% injury; 4, 45% injury; 5, 60% injury; and 6, 75% injury and greater.

cultivars (72.7%) of climbing beans were sensitive to ozone under field conditions. No relationship was found between seed colour and sensitivity to ozone.

Discussion

The use of the dwarf tomato cultivar Tiny Tim in greenhouse experiments allows the intensive study of the effects of repeated exposures to low con-centrations of ozone on the growth, development and yield of a plant from seedling to yield in a 2–3-month time span. We have shown that root and shoot growth and development and yields are significantly depressed by ozone. This depressant effect of ozone has been observed with other plants (Feder, 1970, 1973; Heggestad & Heck, 1971; Manning, Feder & Papia *et al.*, 1972), but not as intensively as reported here. The depressant effect of ozone on yields appeared to relate to interference with fruit set and premature senescence of immature fruit (Table 7). This may relate to ozone effects on pollen and/or pollination; pollen germination and tube elongation are known to be affected by ozone (Feder, 1968; Harrison & Feder, 1974).

Suppression of most of the ozone injury on the sensitive bean cultivar Tempo by benomyl foliar sprays made it possible to determine the effects of ambient concentrations of ozone on the yield of this cultivar under field conditions. These results quantitatively confirm the hypothesis that ozone injury in the field can cause accelerated plant maturity and yield reductions (Landau & Brandt, 1970). Failure of benomyl sprays significantly to affect yields of the resistant cultivar Tenderwhite indicates that the increase in yields of benomyl-sprayed Tempo plants was most likely due to suppression of most of the ozone injury.

Little agreement was observed between results obtained under greenhouse and field conditions for sensitivity of bean cultivars to ozone. This suggests that results from greenhouse screening tests are perhaps not reliable in predicting the sensitivity of bean cultivars to ozone under outdoor conditions. Flower and seed colours were also of little value in predicting ozone sensitivity of bean cultivars under field conditions. It has been widely reported that plants with white flowers are more sensitive to ozone than are those with darker-coloured flowers. This generalisation did not apply for the bean cultivars evaluated, e.g. nine of the ten cultivars with lavender flowers were sensitive to ozone at ambient concentrations. It can be concluded, however, that bean cultivars with trailing or climbing habits are more likely to be sensitive to ozone injury than are those with bushy habits.

While information is available on the effects of low levels of ozone on the growth, development and yield of plants, it is largely obtained from growth chamber, greenhouse and field chamber studies. The results may be relevant only to the conditions of the experiment and can be viewed as indications of the possible effects of ozone. The use of benomyl, and other chemical compounds, to suppress ozone injury allows field experiments to be conducted under more natural conditions, but still introduces an artificial element into the system. The comparison of closely related plant cultivars or isolines differing in sensitivity to ozone would provide the best and most relevant answers to the question of whether ozone injury has any significant effects on the growth, development and yield of economic plants. Unfortunately, little time has been spent looking for such plant cultivars or developing appropriate isolines.

References

Davis, D. D. & Kress, L. (1974). The relative susceptibility of ten bean varieties to ozone. *Plant Disease Reporter* **58**, 14–16.

Evans, L. S. (1973). Bean leaf growth response to moderate ozone levels. *Environmental Pollution* **4**, 17–26.

Feder, W. A. (1968). Reduction in tobacco pollen germination and tube elongation induced by low levels of ozone. *Science* **160**, 1122.

Feder, W. A. (1970). Plant response to chronic exposure of low levels of oxidant-type air pollution. *Environmental Pollution* **1**, 73–9.

Feder, W. A. (1973). Cumulative effects of chronic exposure of plants to low levels of air pollutants. In *Air pollution damage to vegetation, Advances in Chemistry Series No. 122*, Ed. J. A. Naegele, pp. 21–30. American Chemical Society, Washington.

Gentile, A. G., Feder, W. A., Young, R. E. & Santer, Z. (1971). Susceptibility of *Lycopersicon* spp. to ozone injury. *Journal of the American Society of Horticultural Science* **96**, 94–6.

Harrison, B. H. & Feder, W. A. (1974). Ultra-structural changes in pollen exposed to ozone. *Phytopathology* **64**, 257–8.

Heggestad, H. E. & Heck, W. W. (1971). Nature, extent and variation of plant response to air pollutants. *Advances in Agronomy* **23**, 111–45.

Hill, A. C., Pack, M. R., Treshow, M., Downs, R. J. & Transtrum, L. G. (1961). Plant injury induced by ozone. *Phytopathology* **51**, 356–63.

Hindawi, I. J. (1970) *Air pollution injury to vegetation*. National Air Pollution Control Admin. Publication No. A.P. 71, Raleigh, North Carolina, USA, 44 pp.

Howell, R. K. (1972). Differential responses of bean cultivars to ozone and ambient air. *HortScience* **5**, 334 (abstract).

Jacobson, J. S. & Hill, A. C. (1970). *Recognition of air pollution injury to vegetation: a pictorial atlas*. Informative Report No. 1 of the TR7 Agricultural Committee, Air Pollution Control Association, Pittsburgh, Pennsylvania, USA, 109 pp.

Landau, E. & Brandt, C. S. (1970). The use of surveys to estimate air pollution damage to agriculture. *Environmental Research* **3**, 54–61.

Manning, W. J., Feder, W. A. & Papia, P. M. (1972). Influence of long-term low levels of ozone and benomyl on growth and nodulation of Pinto bean plants. *Phytopathology* **62**, 497 (abstract).

Manning, W. J., Feder, W. A. & Vardaro, P. M. (1974). Suppression of oxidant injury by benomyl: effects on yields of bean cultivars in the field. *Journal of Environmental Quality* **3**, 1–3.

Manning, W. J. & Vardaro, P. M. (1974). Ozone and *Pyrenochaeta lycopersici*: effects on growth and development of tomato plants. *Phytopathology* **64**, 582 (abstract).

Manning, W. J. & Vardaro, P. M. (1975). Sensitivity of bean cultivars to low levels of ozone and ambient oxidants. *Annual Proceedings of the American Phytopathological Society*, in press.

Stern, A. C. (1962). *Air pollution, vol. I*. Academic Press, New York & London.

Tomlinson, H. & Rich, S. (1973). Relating ozone resistance to antisenescence in beans treated with benzimidazole. *Phytopathology* **63**, 208 (abstract).

**E.NIEBOER, D.H.S.RICHARDSON,
K.J.PUCKETT & F.D.TOMASSINI**

The phytotoxicity of sulphur dioxide in relation to measurable responses in lichens

Introduction

The damaging effect of air pollution on lichens has been noted for a little over 100 years (Hawksworth, 1971). The data accumulated on this subject over the past century were reviewed in a recent book entitled *Air pollution and lichens* (see Ferry, Baddeley & Hawksworth, 1973). Since then, a bibliography of more recent papers has appeared (Hawksworth, 1974) and is a useful supplementary source of information. The observations to date on the effects of air pollution on lichens may be separated into three broad categories and each is briefly summarised.

The first category involves studies on the distribution and abundance of lichens around industrial and urban complexes. The results have been correlated with measured levels of pollutants to show that sulphur dioxide is the prime cause of the disappearance of lichens from urban areas. However, the dryness of the environment and lack of suitable substrata are also important. Grindon (1859) and Nylander (1866) were the first to note that smoke and gaseous emissions cause a decrease in lichen numbers. Little further work was done until 1926 when Sernander developed the concept of zones of lichen development around cities. He delineated a lichen desert, a struggle zone, and a normal zone. It was also noted that a few lichen species were pollution-tolerant and others, e.g. *Usnea* and *Lobaria*, were extremely sensitive. From this developed many studies in which lichens at different sites, but on comparable substrates (e.g. the boles of particular species of deciduous trees), were examined. The frequency, number and known sensitivity of each species were recorded and from this an index of atmospheric purity calculated for each site (see Moore, 1974; Hawksworth, 1973). Maps showing the degree of pollution as measured by this biological index have also been correlated with absolute measurements of sulphur dioxide at a few points and the data used in planning urban developments (see Ferry *et al.*, 1973). Another approach to distribution studies is based on observations of the presence or absence of key indicator species and this enabled mapping of air quality of the whole of Britain to be carried out in a single summer with the help of 10 000 volunteers (Mabey, 1974). The mapping of lichens has now been completed for more than 100 industrial and urban centres (Ferry *et al.*, 1973). These studies demonstrate that the lichen flora begins to deteriorate within a few months following the onset of a new potent pollution source, but that recovery following the closure of a factory or implementation of clean air control is much slower (see Richardson, 1975). Although such studies do not set out to determine the effects of air pollution on lichen metabolism, they do provide a mass of data to show that lichens are amongst the most pollution-sensitive plants, and potentially most valuable as monitors of changes in the levels of air pollution.

The second type of study involves transplanting lichens into an urban or industrial area from rural sites. The changes that develop in the appearance, growth or physiology of the lichens are then recorded. This work has enabled an estimate to be made of the severity of air pollution in a region by observing the rapidity of such changes. It has also allowed a study of the effects of low levels of sulphur dioxide on lichens over periods of months or years. An example of this type of work is that of LeBlanc & Rao (1973) who cut discs of tree bark colonised by lichens such as *Parmelia sulcata*. These were then nailed to supporting boards erected at increasing distances from the city of Sudbury in Ontario where nickel smelters emit large amounts of sulphur dioxide. After one year it was observed that the lichens had progressively changed colour from greyish green to whitish as one moved from the lightly to the heavily polluted zone. This change was apparently accompanied by the secretion of waxy deposits on the surface of the lichen and also by increasing death and plasmolysis of the algal cells. The macroscopic observations correlated well with decreases in the measured amounts of extractable chlorophyll. The authors also observed increased production of vegetative propagules (soredia) in areas of intermediate pollution. This feature is often noted in lichens occurring naturally in such places.

The third approach is to bring lichens into the laboratory to examine the effects of sulphur dioxide or other substances over periods of minutes or hours. The aim of such research is to discover why lichens are so sensitive and to elucidate the mechanisms of damage and recovery under various conditions. The early studies showed that lichens became discoloured and that brown spots developed in the algal chloroplasts following exposure to 5 ppm or more of sulphur dioxide (Pearson & Skye, 1965; Rao & LeBlanc, 1966). Such levels are abnormally high. However, later Nash (1973) investigated the effects of 0.5–4.0 ppm sulphur dioxide on lichens. He found the limit of sensitivity as measured by reduction in chlorophyll levels was 0.5 ppm for 12 h, and concluded that this could account for the absence of sensitive species such as *Parmelia caperata* from city centres. In general, his data suggested that, over the short term, lichens were no more sensitive than higher plants. However, he pointed out that the ability of lichens to absorb pollutants efficiently would account for the disappearance of these plants from regions where there were continuous low levels of sulphur dioxide pollution. Showman (1972) investigated the effects of sulphur dioxide on lichens and isolated lichen algae, exposing his specimens to 2–4 ppm in dry air or 6 ppm at 50% relative humidity. Although the cultured algae showed physiological upset, the small amount of damage to the lichens exposed to these levels probably reflects the fact that lichens are resistant to sulphur dioxide when dry (Türk, Wirth & Lange, 1974). Margot (1973) studied the soredia of lichens which consist of algal cells surrounded by a loose weft of fungal filaments. He found that the soredia of *Hypogymnia physodes* were killed in greater numbers when exposed to fixed levels of sulphur dioxide at increasing relative humidity. Elegant studies have also been done in Professor Lange's laboratory on the effects of sulphur dioxide on gas exchange by lichens (Türk *et al.*, 1974). There was a marked decrease in assimilation following exposure to 0.2 ppm (0.5 mg SO_2 m^{-3}) sulphur dioxide for 14 h at 10 °C. The most sensitive species investigated was *Lobaria pulmonaria*. In contrast, pollution-tolerant species such as *Xanthoria parientia* showed little or no impairment when exposed to four times the above concentration. Thalli of *Lobaria* and *Xanthoria* in control experiments had net photosynthetic rates of around 2.0 mg CO_2 h^{-1} per g dry wt (at 10 °C, 20 000 lux) and dark respiration rates of 0.6–0.7 mg CO_2 h^{-1} per g dry wt. Immediately following exposure to sulphur dioxide, there was not only a reduction in net assimilation rate, but also a marked increase in respiration rate in those samples kept in the dark. Respiration rates settled down to values between 60–100% of the control samples after a recovery period of 25 days. Baddeley, Ferry & Finegan (1973) found that respiration rates were reduced during the incubation in sulphur dioxide solutions. They used lichens that were vacuum-infiltrated with water and measured the concentration of dissolved oxygen using an oxygen electrode. As lichen algae make up only about 5% of the thallus, it is probable that observed changes in respiration rate represent the reaction of the fungal partner to sulphur dioxide. The fact that lichens varied in their response may be interpreted to mean that the fungal partner may differ in sensitivity. However, there is evidence to show that it is normally the alga which is the more sensitive of the two symbionts. Hill (1971, 1974) examined the effects of sulphite on various aspects of lichen metabolism. As his results complement our own research they are discussed later in this paper.

Lichen response studies

Effect of sulphur dioxide on photosynthetic ^{14}C fixation

The experimental procedure employed in our laboratory in ^{14}C fixation studies consists of pre-incubating a sample of lichen material in an aqueous sulphur dioxide medium of definite volume, concentration and pH for a specified period of time. ^{14}C fixation rates are evaluated either immediately after this exposure, or after a recovery period. The samples are then killed and extracted in 80% boiling ethanol. This forms the ethanol-soluble fraction while the residue comprises the ethanol-insoluble fraction. The amounts of radioactivity in these fractions and in the incubation media are subsequently measured with a thin-end window gas flow Geiger–Müller counter. For details, see Puckett, Nieboer, Flora & Richardson (1973) and Puckett, Richardson, Flora & Nieboer (1974).

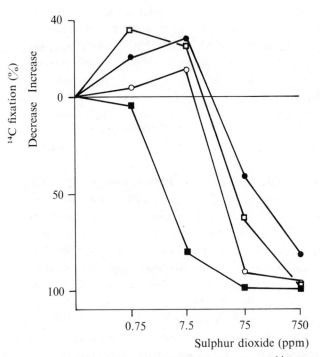

Fig. 1.   The percentage reduction in net ^{14}C fixation by various lichens pre-incubated for 6 h in solutions of sulphur dioxide buffered at pH 4.4, as compared with control samples without sulphur dioxide. Each point represents the mean of six replicates. □, *Cladonia deformis*; ●, *Stereocaulon paschale*; ○, *Umbilicaria muhlenbergii*; ■, *C. alpestris*. (Reproduced with permission from Puckett *et al.* (1973); the curve for *C. alpestris* was incorrectly plotted in the original figure.)

Experiments using the technique described above have shown that sensitivity to sulphur dioxide varies with the lichen species (Figs 1 and 2), and becomes more pronounced with increasing acidity and sulphur dioxide concentration. Similar findings have been reported in studies with sodium pyrosulphite (Hill, 1971, 1974; Türk *et al.*, 1974). As mentioned earlier, a reduction in net photosynthesis has also been observed in carbon dioxide exchange measurements following exposures of lichen samples to gaseous

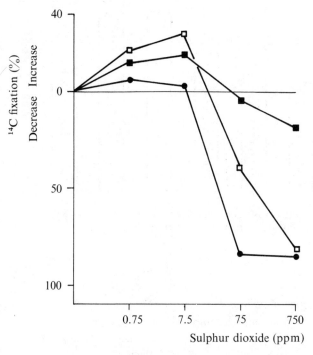

Fig. 2.   The percentage reduction in net ^{14}C fixation by *Stereocaulon paschale* incubated for 6 h in solutions of sulphur dioxide buffered at various pH values, as compared with control samples without sulphur dioxide. Each point represents the mean of six replicates. ■, pH 6.6; □, pH 4.4; ●, pH 3.2.

sulphur dioxide (Türk *et al.*, 1974). Hence, it is evident that measurement of net photosynthesis affords a rapid and sensitive technique for evaluating the relative sensitivities of lichens to sulphur dioxide. We have recently determined the relative ^{14}C fixation rates of lichen species collected from the MacKenzie Valley, North-West Territories (NWT), Canada (Richardson *et al.*, 1974). The histogram in Fig. 3 summarises one such comparison for six lichen species obtained from Fort Simpson, NWT. As in Fig. 1, *Stereocaulon*

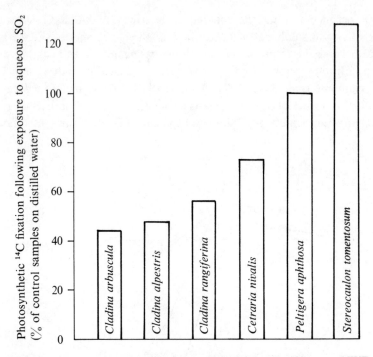

Fig. 3.   Relative sensitivity of lichens collected from Fort Simpson, NWT, to aqueous sulphur dioxide (25 ppm, unbuffered pH 3.5, 10-min exposure).

Table 1.   *The effect of light and moisture on the recovery of photosynthetic* ^{14}C *fixation in* Umbilicaria muhlenbergii

	^{14}C fixation*			
	Light and moist[a]	Light and dry[a]	Dark and moist[b]	Dark and dry[b]
Control	22.5 ± 2.0	35.6 ± 2.4	71.8 ± 4.0	60.7 ± 3.2
Sulphur dioxide	22.3 ± 3.6	11.3 ± 1.3	44.7 ± 4.3	6.5 ± 0.5
% recovery	99.0%	31.7%	62.2%	10.7%

* Amount of ^{14}C incorporated (cpm × 10^4) by ten 5-mm discs subsequent to periods of exposure (15 min in 75 ppm SO_2 at pH 3) and recovery (24 h, under different conditions of light and moisture).

[a,b] Separate experiments carried out on different dates. From Puckett *et al.* (1974).

sp. appears to be considerably more robust than the other species; indeed, the pre-incubation in sulphur dioxide enhanced its relative fixation rate, while a 50% reduction was observed for *Cladina* spp. Türk *et al.* (1974) have noted, however, that different lichen sensitivity orders may be obtained for gaseous as opposed to aqueous exposures, for reasons outlined in the section on the mechanisms of phytotoxicity and recovery (p. 77).

Considerable evidence is now available to show that lichen species can recover from the effects of sulphur dioxide. This ability would appear to be most pronounced for the least sensitive lichens (Richardson *et al.*, 1974), and appears optimal when conditions are suitable for lichen photosynthesis (i.e. light and moist), as illustrated in Table 1. Hill (1974) and Türk *et al.* (1974) have also observed recovery by lichens from depressed net photosynthesis, although the dependence on moisture and light conditions was

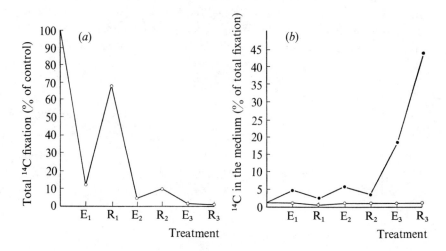

Fig. 4. (*a*) The effect of repeated exposures to aqueous sulphur dioxide on the total photosynthetic ^{14}C fixation of *Umbilicaria muhlenbergii*.
E, exposure for 15 min in 75 ppm, pH 3, 18 °C; R, 6-h recovery period on moist filter paper in the light at 18 °C. ^{14}C fixation rates were measured immediately after each E and R period. Reproduced with permission from Puckett *et al.* (1974). (*b*) The effect of repeated exposures to aqueous sulphur dioxide on the proportion of the fixed ^{14}C found in the photosynthetic medium. ○, control; ●, discs treated with sulphur dioxide. Details as for (*a*). Reproduced with permission from Puckett *et al.* (1974).

not examined. Repeated exposures culminate in complete metabolic inactivity (Fig. 4*a* and *b*). The marked increase in the proportion of photosynthate released into the medium after the third and fatal exposure signals the severity of the damage incurred.

Potassium efflux studies

Recently we reported that sulphur dioxide induced the leakage of potassium ions (K^+) into the incubation medium (Puckett *et al.*, 1974). In samples exposed to aqueous sulphur dioxide for 15 min (75 ppm, pH 3), potassium losses after the 24-h recovery period were only slightly above control values. Losses remained high for those exposed for 60 min. Under the same conditions, recoveries based on ^{14}C fixation studies were 99% and 33% respectively. Extensive studies, summarised below, have now been completed to determine the potential of potassium as a measurable parameter for assessing sulphur dioxide damage.

The experimental procedure employed in the K^+ efflux studies is as follows. Lichen material (e.g. 150 mg) is incubated in a small volume (e.g. 12 ml) of aqueous sulphur dioxide solution for a definite time period. The sample is then removed by filtration and the filtrate diluted to a volume (e.g. 50 ml) suitable for analysis by atomic absorption or flame emission photometry. Control samples are incubated in dilute hydrochloric acid solutions

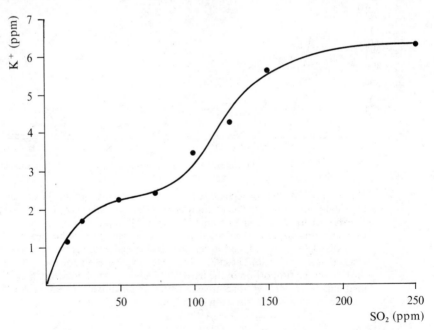

Fig. 5.   Potassium release by 150 mg of *Cladina rangiferina* incubated for 3 h in 12 ml of aqueous sulphur dioxide of various concentrations. The K^+ concentrations are corrected for background release observed in control samples at the same pH, and refer to a final volume of 50 ml (see text for details).

of the same pH. The dependence of the amount of K$^+$ found in the medium on the sulphur dioxide concentration is depicted in Fig. 5 for *Cladina rangiferina*. It is evident that the release is biphasic. In this feature it resembles the rate (amount per unit weight per unit time) of absorption of potassium by barley roots as a function of the concentration of potassium chloride in the solution (Epstein, 1972). In most lichen systems we have examined the first release stage follows a limited form of the Michaelis–Menten equation as shown by the linear relationship between the amount of K$^+$ released per unit weight of lichen per unit time and the reciprocal of the sulphur dioxide concentration (Fig. 6). The second stage adheres only roughly to this linear

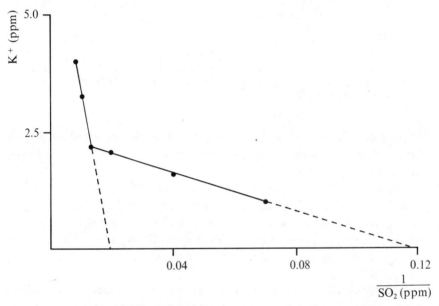

Fig. 6.   Limiting Michaelis–Menten equation for the potassium efflux data of Fig. 5.

relationship, and in some cases appears multi-phasic. According to the Langmuir adsorption isotherm, this single reciprocal form of the Michaelis–Menten equation implies that the rate of K$^+$ efflux is determined by conditions where the adsorbing surface is nearly completely covered with aqueous sulphur dioxide molecules, or that the available binding or carrier sites are virtually occupied to capacity (Glasstone, 1946).

The linear segments in Fig. 6 are readily extrapolated to threshold sulphur dioxide concentrations. Values of 8.5 ppm and 53 ppm were obtained for the first and second stage respectively. These limiting concentrations are characteristic for *C. rangiferina*, with the lower value marking the lowest

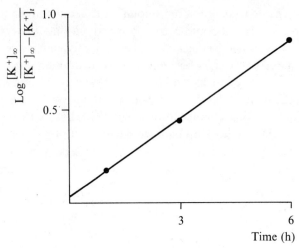

Fig. 7.   A first-order rate plot of potassium release by *Cladina rangiferina* (150 mg sample in 12 ml) during exposure to aqueous sulphur dioxide (75 ppm, pH 3.0).

sulphur dioxide concentration inducing K^+ efflux for the stated conditions. Consequently, a new and comprehensive sensitivity scale may be established for lichens on this basis.

The dependence of potassium efflux on time could be treated as a first-order rate plot (Fig. 7). This demonstrates that the K^+ release process is controlled by diffusion, as has been observed for the non-metabolic uptake of metal ions by lichens (Nieboer, Puckett & Grace, 1976). The observed effective rate constant is 0.31 h^{-1} (for 150 mg of *C. rangiferina* in 12 ml of 75 ppm SO_2 at pH 3).

It is premature to assign the two separate efflux stages to two distinct mechanisms of sulphur dioxide attack or uptake (cf. discussion of K^+ uptake by barley roots in Epstein, 1972). However, in a preliminary study, we have examined thin sections of *U. muhlenbergii* cut from material stained with cobaltinitrite and sulphide, which when applied consecutively provide a histological stain for K^+ (Allaway & Hsiao, 1973). Sulphur dioxide would appear to induce the release of this ion from both symbionts, and this in principle could account for the two release stages.

Lichen pigment studies

Sulphur dioxide is known to induce three distinct in-vivo changes in extractable lichen pigments; namely, bleaching, phaeophytinisation, and the process responsible for a blue shift of the pigment spectrum (maximum shift of 10 nm). These are illustrated in Fig. 8. It is our practice to extract the pigments with hot pyridine, after a chosen pre-treatment of the lichen material (Puckett *et al.*, 1973). Two 3-ml extractions followed by single 2-ml and 1-ml extractions were found to be adequate for 0.6 g samples. The combined extracts are then diluted to 50 ml with 80% acetone. The presence of

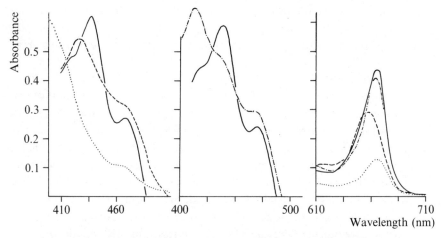

Fig. 8.   In-vivo effect of sulphur dioxide on lichen pigments. Spectra are representative of extracted pigments for: control samples from *C. rangiferina* (————); SO₂-induced phaeophytinisation, from *C. rangiferina* (—·—·—·—); SO₂-induced shift, from *P. aphthosa* (— — — — —); SO₂-induced bleaching, from *C. rangiferina* (· · · · · · · · · · ·). Spectra were chosen so that the relative intensities are 'roughly' significant.

pyridine in 80% acetone has no effect on the position of the absorption maxima in the visible spectrum of the extracted pigments.

The exact nature of the in-vivo effect of sulphur dioxide on lichen pigments varies considerably from one species to another. For example, *U. muhlenbergii* and *C. rangiferina* both contain the alga *Trebouxia* (Ahmadjian, 1967) and yet the observed changes differ greatly. Thus, incubation for 6 h at 18 °C and 8500 lux in buffered sulphur dioxide solutions (e.g. 750 ppm, pH 3) results in a 10 nm blue shift for pigments extracted from *U. muhlenbergii*, while both phaeophytinisation and bleaching are predominant for *C. rangiferina*. In the same medium, the pigments of *Peltigera aphthosa* (which contains the alga *Coccomyxa*) are susceptible to both the 10 nm spectral shift and mild bleaching. It is worth noting that the bleaching was virtually absent for samples of *C. rangiferina* incubated in the same medium in the absence of light.

As indicated in the Introduction, and as shown in the section on the comparison of K^+ efflux with other responses (p. 73), the quantitative

72   E. NIEBOER AND OTHERS

evaluation of chlorophyll content of lichen samples exposed to sulphur dioxide is another parameter by which to measure their response to this pollutant. It should be emphasised that expressing the amount of chlorophyll in lichens, after fumigation with sulphur dioxide, as a percentage of the sum of chlorophylls plus phaeophytins on a per gram dry weight basis (e.g. Nash, 1973) disregards any pigment loss due to bleaching. The lichen may be considerably more sensitive to pigment destruction than indicated in such studies, especially if the species is susceptible to bleaching (e.g. *C. rangiferina*).

Aqueous versus *gaseous sulphur dioxide concentration*

One criticism of exposure studies in aqueous sulphur dioxide solutions has been the use of concentrations believed to be unrealistic from the point of view of known atmospheric levels. The biological correlation between the effect of aqueous and gaseous exposures established by Saunders (1966) on the basis of work with the fungal spores of *Diplocarpon rosae* is often quoted (e.g. Puckett *et al.*, 1973; Tanaka, Takanashi & Yatazawa, 1974). Atmospheric levels as determined by this biological scale are considered to be a thousand-fold less than aqueous concentrations. The results reported in Fig. 9 are based on experiments devised to establish a less subjective relationship.

Fifteen to thirty millilitres of distilled water in a Petri dish were equilibrated with gaseous sulphur dioxide at 18 °C in the light (8500 lux) for 24 h by passing a stream of dry air containing known concentrations (ppm, v/v) of sulphur

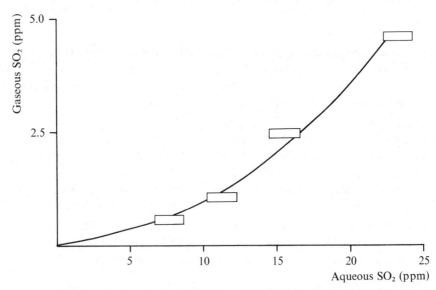

Fig. 9. Experimental relationship between gaseous (ppm, v/v) and aqueous (ppm, wt/wt) concentrations of sulphur dioxide at 18 °C.

dioxide over the dish placed in a 700-ml glass fumigation vessel. The sulphur dioxide in the aqueous solution (ppm, wt/wt) was determined from its final pH, since a reproducible correlation exists between the aqueous sulphur dioxide concentration and pH, over the concentration range 5–80 ppm. This procedure was tested with an independent method of analysis based on the iodine/sulphur dioxide reaction. The gaseous sulphur dioxide levels were determined from the flow rate and the loss in weight of sulphur dioxide from Metronic Dynacal permeation tubes (Metronic Associates, Inc., Palo Alto, California). The final equilibrium concentration of sulphur dioxide in solution was found to be independent of the exact volume of distilled water placed in the Petri dish and independent of the volume of water evaporated during the equilibration period. Equilibrium was established during the first 3 h and attainment of this could be easily followed by adding a few drops of methyl orange indicator to the water before the start of a fumigation.

The non-linearity of the relationship in Fig. 9 mitigates against using a constant conversion factor for relating gaseous and aqueous concentrations. Some numerical values for this relationship expressed as [ppm of SO$_2$ (wt/wt in solution)]:[ppm SO$_2$ (v/v in air)] are 5:0.2, 10:1.0, 20:3.6 and 25:5.7.

It is known that lichens are insensitive to sulphur dioxide when dry (Türk *et al.*, 1974). Water is absorbed over the entire surface and hence a moist lichen can be considered similar to an open water surface in which sulphur dioxide is dissolving. It is our contention that the relationship in Fig. 9 reflects the exchange equilibrium at a wet lichen surface for a lichen subject to atmospheric fumigations. Türk *et al.* found that except for one species (*Xanthoria parietina*), the pH values of the thalli decreased during a 14-h gaseous fumigation at 2 mg m^{-3} (0.8 ppm). In fact, the average observed thallus pH value was 3.9 On the basis of the data in Fig. 9, this gaseous concentration corresponds to an aqueous concentration of 9.0 ppm. This compares well with the·value of 9.5 ppm evaluated from the relationship between pH and aqueous concentration mentioned above.

A comparison of the potassium efflux with other responses

The small rate constants observed for K$^+$ efflux indicate that it is not a very sensitive parameter for assessing the effects of sulphur dioxide during very short exposures. This is borne out by the data in Table 2 for *U. muhlenbergii* which show that K$^+$ is released into the incubation medium only in the more concentrated sulphur dioxide solutions. However, an increase in the incubation time (e.g. 15 min to 3 h; see Table 3 and Fig. 5) is accompanied by the release of this ion even in very dilute solutions. By contrast, a reduction in

Table 2. *Comparison of SO$_2$-induced changes in pigments, and K$^+$ efflux in* U. muhlenbergii

Aqueous SO$_2$ (ppm)	Visible pigment changes[a]	Potassium efflux E[b]	After recovery[c]	% of total[d] lichen K$^+$ lost
10	NC	–	–	0
25	NC	–	–	0
50	NC	Marginal	–	0
125	Brown	+	+	50

[a] Based on changes observed in the greenish lichen discs during the recovery period (R); NC, no change.

[b] K$^+$ found in the exposure (E) medium (–, no leakage; +, leakage).

[c] Lichen was blotted after the recovery period and then equilibrated for 60 min in distilled water. The K$^+$ content of this solution was then evaluated.

[d] Determined by comparing the total K$^+$ content (digestion of sample in perchloric/nitric acid, followed by flame photometry analysis) of exposed samples after the post-recovery washing to that of control samples treated similarly in the absence of sulphur dioxide.

E, 15 min; R, 24 h at 18 °C, 8500 lux.

Table 3. *Comparison of SO$_2$-induced changes in pigments, and K$^+$ efflux in* U. muhlenbergii

Aqueous SO$_2$ (ppm)	Visible pigment changes[a]	Potassium efflux E[b]	R[c]	% of total[d] lichen K$^+$ lost
15	NC	–	–	0
35	NC	+	–	22
75	Brown	+	+	50
150	Brown	+	+	74

[a] Based on changes observed in the greenish lichen discs during the recovery period (R); NC, no change.

[b] K$^+$ found in the exposure (E) medium (–, no leakage; +, leakage).

[c] Lichen material was washed with distilled water after the recovery period and the K$^+$ in the wash evaluated.

[d] Determined by comparing the total K$^+$ content (digestion of sample in perchloric/nitric acid, followed by flame photometry analysis) of exposed samples after the post-recovery washing to that of control samples treated similarly in the absence of sulphur dioxide. The total potassium content of the control samples was found to be c.60 μmol g^{-1} dry wt.

E, 3 h; R, 24 h at 18 °C, 8500 lux.

[14]C fixation would appear to be extremely rapid even in short exposures (Puckett *et al.*, 1973; Hill, 1974); and this appears to be true for respiration (Baddeley *et al.*, 1973). Pigment destruction would appear to be a somewhat slower process. The delayed action of sulphur dioxide, illustrated in Tables 2–5, shows how lethal this substance is to lichens. During recovery, even after very short and mild exposures, K$^+$ is released and pigments are bleached or undergo phaeophytinisation. These events culminate in permanent reduction in net photosynthesis (Table 4) and presumably permanent

Table 4.   *Comparison of SO$_2$-induced changes in pigments, and K$^+$ efflux in* C. rangiferina

Aqueous SO$_2$ (ppm)	Pigment changes[a]	Potassium efflux after recovery[b]	% reduction in ^{14}C fixation[c]	% of photosynthate found in the incubation medium[d]
25	NC	–	19	1.8
75	Bleached	+	96	33
125	Bleached	+	96	38

[a] Evaluated quantitatively by extracting the pigments after the post-recovery potassium leakage test; NC, no change.

[b] Lichen material was blotted after the recovery period (R) and then equilibrated for 60 min in distilled water. The K$^+$ content of this wash solution was then evaluated (–, no leakage; +, leakage).

[c] [14]C fixation rates of samples were determined after the recovery period and then compared to that of controls treated similarly in the absence of sulphur dioxide.

[d] The value for the control samples was 1.8%.

E, 10 min; R, 24 h at 18 °C, 8500 lux.

impairment. The extent of damage incurred is reflected in the considerable loss of a lichen's potassium content during the exposure (Tables 2, 3 and 5), as well as the increased leakiness of the damaged material as judged by the sizeable increase in the proportion of photosynthate appearing in the fixation medium (Fig. 4*a* and *b*; Table 4) and by the residual efflux of potassium after recovery (Tables 2 and 4).

It is obvious that individual lichen species respond to different degrees following a fumigation of specified duration and intensity. By using the parameters discussed, it is possible to characterise the response of each species and its ability to recover. However, since the K$^+$ efflux accompanies all the responses, extrapolation to the threshold sulphur dioxide concentration which will not induce potassium release appears to be a sensitive and simple method of evaluating lichen sensitivity. This applies particularly to studies which call for estimates of the maximum permissible atmospheric sulphur dioxide concentrations over a given time period which will not detrimentally affect the lichen flora, at least in the relatively short-term. In the case of C. rangiferina, this threshold concentration (for a 3-h exposure) was 8.5 ppm, which, according to Fig. 9, is equivalent to an atmospheric concentration of 0.68 ppm or 1790 μg m^{-3}. The data presented for C. alpestris and C. rangiferina in Table 5 for gaseous exposures show that in all cases

Table 5.   Pigment damage and K$^+$ efflux in C. alpestris during gaseous SO$_2$ fumigations

Exposure time (h)	SO$_2$ (ppm, v/v)[c]	Reduction in chlorophyll content[a]	K$^+$ efflux during recovery[b]	Recovery period (h)
6	1	0	+	24
24	1	30	+	24
3	2	0	+[d]	48
6	3	0	+[d]	24
24	2	47	+	24

[a] The chlorophyll content was evaluated from the observed absorbance at 652 nm (Arnon, 1949), and was compared to that of control samples treated similarly in the absence of sulphur dioxide. Pigments were extracted after the recovery period by the pyridine method (see text for details).

[b] The lichen sample was washed with 10 ml of distilled water after the exposure period. The K$^+$ content of the wash was then evaluated and compared to that for control washings.

[c] Determined from the flow rate and the loss in weight of sulphur dioxide from a Dynacal permeation tube. The exposure chamber was identical to that used in determining the data in Fig. 9.

[d] Data refer to C. rangiferina which has sensitivity to sulphur dioxide similar to that of C. alpestris (see Fig. 3).

Experiments were carried out at 18 °C, 8500 lux.

examined K$^+$ efflux does occur even when no chlorophyll damage can be detected. Thus, based on the parameter of potassium release by lichens, it should be possible to specify acceptable atmospheric levels for sulphur dioxide. However, it would seem prudent to choose species of known hypersensitivity in such evaluation.

Hypersensitive species are likely to be those whose distribution correlates, in mapping studies, with a mean annual or winter sulphur dioxide air pollution level of under about 30 μg m^{-3}. Genera such as *Usnea, Lobaria, Sticta, Ramalina* and perhaps *Cladonia* fall into this category (see Hawksworth, 1971). While these very low mean sulphur dioxide levels may affect the above genera in the long-term, the distribution of lichens may be determined more by short bursts of high sulphur dioxide levels that are concealed in average annual values. This is particularly likely where the source of pollution is industrial, as meteorological conditions causing high ground-level concentrations of sulphur dioxide can occur for a few hours periodically throughout the year. The way in which these sorts of fumigations have profound effects on the metabolism of lichens is discussed below.

Mechanisms of phytotoxicity and recovery

Phytotoxicity

The toxicity of sulphur dioxide to plants can be related to its chemistry. Puckett *et al.* (1973) have pointed out that at physiological pH values, dissolved sulphur dioxide can potentially participate in both oxidation (i.e. is itself reduced) and reduction (i.e. is itself oxidised) processes. These conclusions were based on a detailed examination of redox potentials of dissolved sulphur dioxide in relation to pH and concentration. Thus, at pH 7, bisulphite (HSO_3^-) and sulphite (SO_3^{2-}) are nearly equally abundant forms of sulphur dioxide, while at pH 4, the bisulphite ion is predominant. The increase in toxicity as the pH of the sulphur dioxide incubation medium was lowered (see Fig. 2) correlates with the expected increase in oxidising power of the dissolved sulphur dioxide.

The aspects of sulphur dioxide chemistry outlined above indicate that this substance is capable of interfering with the electron flow in the electron transport chains of chloroplast systems I and II, at least from a thermodynamic point of view. In support of the involvement of redox properties, it was demonstrated that bleaching of extracted pigments by sulphur dioxide was identical to that induced by the strong oxidising agent potassium permanganate (Puckett *et al.*, 1973). The same bleaching process has been observed for air-oxidation of chlorophyll in acetone (Johnston & Watson, 1956). It seems reasonable to conclude, therefore, that the in-vivo bleaching of lichen pigments (see Fig. 8; Table 4) is an oxidation process. The exact role of sulphur dioxide in this bleaching phenomenon may be complex as light is also required. Perhaps, this substance induces irreversible photo-oxidation of chlorophylls *in vivo*, rather than a direct attack on these pigments. Sulphur dioxide is known to cause swelling of the thylakoids within the chloroplasts of broad-bean (Wellburn, Majernik & Wellburn, 1972) and in severe fumigations may result in plasmolysis accompanied by swelling of plant chloroplasts (Brandt & Heck, 1968). The photo-oxidation induced by sulphur dioxide would seem to suggest a similar chloroplast disorder of the algal component of lichens. Such damage could also explain the great sensitivity of some lichen species to phaeophytinisation after exposure to the pollutant (see Tables 2 and 3; Fig. 8).

The blue shift in the spectra of pigments from lichens exposed to sulphur dioxide which was reported by Puckett et al. (1973) and demonstrated in Fig. 8, is also very likely to be an oxidation process. Similar spectral changes occur for the allomerisation or auto-oxidation of chlorophyll in vitro when dissolved in methanol (Johnston & Watson, 1956; Holt, 1958; Seeley, 1966; Hynninen & Assandri, 1973). This process is known to involve the attack and oxidation of ring V of chlorophyll*. Copper, administered as Cu^{2+}, is known to bring about the same oxidation process and the accompanying blue shift in chlorophyll extracted from exposed Chlorella vulgaris (Gross, Pugno & Dugger, 1970) and from the lichen U. muhlenbergii (Puckett et al., 1973; Puckett, 1974).

A fundamentally more serious mode of attack of sulphur dioxide on lichens is its ability to cleave disulphide linkages (Puckett et al., 1974, and references cited therein). The reaction is a redox process:

$$RSSR + SO_3^{2-} \rightleftharpoons RSSO_3^- + RS^-.$$

Since the tertiary structure of many enzymes is dependent on the integrity of their disulphide bonds, destruction of this unit would deactivate them. Indeed, Ziegler (1974a) has demonstrated that sulphite causes a splitting of the aggregated form of plant malate dehydrogenase. Similarly, alteration of cell permeability should result from attack by sulphur dioxide on structural proteins which are found in the cell membranes. Some evidence that this occurs comes from the work of Hill (1974) who studied ^{35}S-labelled sulphite uptake by the lichens Usnea spp. and Lecanora conizaeoides. He showed that nearly all the insolubly bound radioactive sulphur could be released by the enzymatic action of protease, and consequently that this sulphite was bound to cell proteins. Puckett et al. (1974) have demonstrated by in-vitro experiments that very low concentrations of dissolved sulphur dioxide are able to deactivate enzymes with and without disulphide bonds. Thus, other centres in a protein must be susceptible to attack by sulphur dioxide, and one plausible interpretation is rendered below.

* Attack of the vinyl group at the 2-position of chlorophyll should not be completely ruled out as modification of this group could be accompanied by a blue shift (Seeley, 1966; Scheer & Katz, 1974).

A potential deactivation mechanism stems from the ability of sulphite ions to form rather stable metal complexes (Sillén & Martell, 1964, 1971). Sulphite, in contrast to sulphate, is a strong ligand especially with respect to transition metal ions (Williams, 1973). For example, it is known that it binds strongly to open-sided iron haem-containing enzyme centres (Williams, 1973), as well as to compounds related to vitamin B$_{12}$ (Haywood et al., 1965; Hill, 1974). Thus sulphite may be able to block electron transfer and other metallo-enzyme mediated processes. It is interesting that Ziegler (1974b) has shown for malate dehydrogenase, that the sulphite inhibition pattern with respect to malate and manganese ions (Mn^{2+}) reveals a close interrelation between the binding of both these reactants and sulphite. This work was done on the enzyme from Zea mays and which is known to require Mn^{2+} (Mahler & Cordes, 1966).

The destruction of protein structure is consistent with the observations of cytoplasmic leakage of potassium (Fig. 5; Tables 2–5) and of photosynthate (Fig. 4b). Such destruction has been used to explain changes in the permeability of protoplasmic membranes in higher plant cells and the reduced enzyme activity accompanying sulphur dioxide exposures (see Puckett et al., 1974). The observed curtailment of photosynthesis and respiration could be explained by this attack on proteins, though the blocking of metal binding sites in redox systems and interference with electron flow must also be considered.

Sulphite is also able to compete for the carbon dioxide or bicarbonate binding sites in the enzymes of carbon fixation. Inhibition studies of ribulose-1,5-diphosphate carboxylase in spinach (Ziegler, 1972), of malate dehydrogenase in Zea mays (Ziegler, 1974b) and phosphoenolpyruvate carboxylase in Zea mays (Ziegler, 1973) leave no doubt of this. Such competitive inhibition with one of the substrates may also be important in phosphorylation (see Sij & Swanson, 1974; Puckett et al., 1973).

One other well-known reaction of aqueous sulphur dioxide has been shown to be involved in its phytotoxicity. This is the formation of bisulphite addition products. The bisulphite ion readily adds to most aldehydes, methylketones and unhindered cyclic ketones (Allinger et al., 1971). This reaction is reversible, and thus it seems to us that such addition compounds could serve as useful sulphite storage vehicles. It is not surprising therefore, that glyoxylate bisulphite is equally as effective an enzyme inhibitor as sulphite (Mukerji & Yang, 1974). The formation of glyoxylate bisulphite in plant leaves exposed to sulphur dioxide appears confirmed (Tanaka, Takanashi & Yatazawa, 1972a) and in itself may be responsible for inhibiting those pathways in which glyoxylate is an intermediate (Tanaka, Takanashi, Kadota & Yatazawa, 1972b).

Mechanisms of recovery

The recovery of lichens was found to be optimal under conditions conducive to photosynthesis (Table 1). Metabolic involvement is therefore implied. This is not surprising since most plants are able to metabolise sulphite and its oxidation product sulphate (Schiff & Hodson, 1973). Indeed, the sulphur contents of lichens growing in sulphur dioxide rich environments have been found to be considerably higher than those found in lichens growing outside such a pollution zone (Gilbert, 1969; Bowen, 1970; Richardson *et al.*, 1975). An excess has been noted of both oxidised sulphur (as sulphate: LeBlanc, 1969) in lichens, and reduced sulphur groups (as water-soluble sulphydryl groups in spruce needles: Härtell, 1973: Grill & Esterbauer, 1973). In addition, the involvement of lichen metabolism in sulphur dioxide detoxification after a fumigation, finds support in the significant increase observed in dark respiration during the initial recovery period (Türk *et al.*, 1974).

The removal of sulphur dioxide should return a system to normal when competitive inhibition is the mode of attack because such inhibition should be reversible. The same is likely to be true for the binding of sulphite to metal centres. The redox properties of sulphur dioxide may aid in its removal from the metal binding sites of metalloproteins with redox functions. The return to normal respiration and photosynthetic rates (Table 1; Türk *et al.*, 1974), as well as the cessation of the K^+ leakage (Tables 2–4) following mild exposures, imply that a lichen is able to overcome the damage incurred during and immediately after fumigation by sulphur dioxide (cf. the delaying action of sulphur dioxide, Tables 2–4). This is to be expected in view of the mechanisms discussed above, as well as the fact that the disulphide bond cleavage in proteins is known to be at least partially reversible.

Ecological aspects of toxicity

It is evident that there are several ways in which sulphur dioxide can bring about metabolic upset in lichens and more than one mechanism of detoxification. Aside from metabolically mediated recovery mechanisms, there are other ways in which lichens may resist the effects of sulphur dioxide. Türk *et al.* (1974) discuss these under the term 'stress avoidance' and they include: (*a*) swelling of the lichen tissues; (*b*) variations in thallus structure; and (*c*) a covering of soredia which are not easily wettable. Thus, for example, sulphur dioxide uptake may be slowed following swelling due to water uptake in species with a dense cortex. Also, crustose lichens which have a relatively small exposed surface, are generally more resistant than foliose forms while fruticose lichens are most sensitive. Türk *et al.* (1974) also comment that lichens in the last group, from polluted areas, have a thicker thallus; while

LeBlanc & Rao (1973) observed the secretion of waxy substances under these conditions. In addition, several workers (Gilbert, 1969; Syratt & Wanstall, 1969; Türk et al., 1974) have pointed out that substrate–lichen interactions are important. It is well-documented that lichens penetrate further into sulphur dioxide fumigated regions when growing on basic substrates than when growing on acid substrates. This observation correlates with the increased toxicity noted in response studies as the pH of the exposure medium is lowered. It is also consistent with an increase in the oxidising power and a reduction in the ionic charge (HSO_3^- versus SO_3^{2-}) of dissolved sulphur dioxide.

The intensity and duration of a fumigation determines the amount of sulphur dioxide accumulated. In relation to the buffering capacity of the cells, this will determine the effective internal pH of the cells and thus the specific toxicity mechanisms that are operative. Lichens differ from higher plants in that they absorb over their entire surface when moist, rapidly accumulating substances from air or water (Tuominen & Jaakkola, 1973; Nieboer, Puckett & Grace, 1976). It is therefore readily evident why lichens have been observed (in distribution studies) to be so sensitive to the presence of sulphur dioxide (see Ferry et al., 1973). Dry lichens have proved to be very resistant to damage by this pollutant (Türk et al., 1974), and hence the microclimate in which a species grows may be extremely important. Indeed this may explain, at least in part, the hypersensitivity of lichens in the genera Lobaria and Sticta which are typically found in habitats that are almost constantly moist.

Another important consideration is that lichens are a symbiosis between two different organisms; a fungus and an alga. For example, mechanisms of recovery dependent on energy-rich compounds, such as ATP, derived from photophosphorylation, will not be available to the fungal partner. In addition, the symbiosis is successful only when the delicate metabolic balance between the two partners is maintained. The importance of this is reflected in the difficulty of resynthesising lichens from their two components in the laboratory. This has only been achieved recently (see Ahmadjian, 1973). Early experiments had resulted in the breakdown of the symbiosis and death of one partner. The observation that the distribution of certain lichen species is adversely affected by average atmospheric concentrations of sulphur dioxide less than 30 μg m^{-3} over a long period, may be explained in terms of a slight shift in the metabolic balance when one partner is affected but not immediately killed by the phytotoxic mechanisms outlined in this paper. Under conditions where acute and chronic injury are observed, resulting from the high levels of sulphur dioxide that occur periodically around urban and industrial centres, the phytotoxic mechanisms no doubt directly cause the death of one or both partners. The symptoms of such damage include death or disintegration of the central parts of foliose thalli or bleaching of the young actively growing tips of lichens (Gilbert, 1969; R. E. Showman, personal communication).

In conclusion, the effects of sulphur dioxide on lichens are clearly complex but their elucidation provides one of the most fascinating problems of lichenology, particularly as it involves both applied and pure research of a type that bridges the gaps between chemistry and biology.

The research reported in this paper was supported by grants from the National Research Council of Canada (Nos. A6036, A6419) and a contract from Atmospheric Environment Services, Environment Canada.

Addendum

The data in Fig. 9 comply with the relationship:

$$\text{ppm SO}_2 \text{ (wt/wt in solution)} = 10.3[\text{ppm SO}_2(\text{v/v in air})]^{\frac{1}{2}}$$

References

Ahmadjian, V. (1967). A guide to the algae occurring as lichen symbionts: isolation, culture, cultural physiology and identification. *Phycologia* **6**, 128–60.

Ahmadjian, V. (1973). Resynthesis of lichens. In *The lichens*, Eds V. Ahmadjian & M. E. Hale, pp. 565–80. Academic Press, New York & London.

Allaway, W. G. & Hsiao, T. C. (1973). Preparation of rolled epidermis of *Vicia faba* L. so that stomata are the only viable cells. Analysis of guard cell potassium by flame photometry. *Australian Journal of Biological Science* **26**, 309–18.

Allinger, N. L., Cava, M. P., De Jongh, D. C., Johnson, C. R., Lebel, N. A. & Stevens, C. L. (1971). *Organic chemistry*, p. 480. Worth Publishers, New York.

Arnon, D. I. (1949). Copper enzymes in isolated chloroplasts. Polyphenoloxidase in *Beta vulgaris*. *Plant Physiology* **24**, 1–15.

Baddeley, M. S., Ferry, B. W. & Finegan, E. J. (1973). Sulphur dioxide and respiration in lichens. In *Air pollution and lichens*, Eds B. W. Ferry, M. S. Baddeley & D. L. Hawksworth, pp. 299–313. Athlone Press, London.

Bowen, H. J. M. (1970). Determination of sulphate ion by replacement of iodate in iodine-131 labelled barium iodate. *Analyst* **95**, 665–7.

Brandt, C. S. & Heck, W. W. (1968). Effects of air pollutants on vegetation. In *Air pollution*, Ed. A. C. Stern, **1**, 401–43. Academic Press, New York & London.

Epstein, E. (1972). *Mineral nutrition of plants: principles and perspectives*, pp. 103–50. Wiley, New York.

Ferry, B. W., Baddeley, M. S. & Hawksworth, D. L. (1973). *Air pollution and lichens*. Athlone Press, London. 389 pp.

Gilbert, O. L. (1969). The effect of SO$_2$ on lichens and bryophytes around Newcastle-upon-Tyne. In *Air pollution. Proceedings of the first European congress on the influence of air pollution on animals and plants, 1968*, pp. 223–35. Centre for Agricultural Publishing and Documentation, Wageningen.

Glasstone, S. (1946). *Physical chemistry* 2nd edition, pp. 1198–1200. Van Nostrand, New York.

Grill, D. & Esterbauer, H. (1973). Cysteine und glutathion in gesunden und SO$_2$-geschädigten Fichtennadeln. *European Journal of Forestry and Pathology* **3**, 65–71.

Grindon, L. H. (1859). *The Manchester flora*. W. White, London.

Gross, R. E., Pugno, P. & Dugger, W. M. (1970). Observations on the mechanisms of copper damage in *Chlorella*. *Plant Physiology* **46**, 183–5.

Härtell, O. (1973). The action of sulphur dioxide on plant cells. (Paper presented at the 2nd International Plant Pathological Congress, Minneapolis, USA, 1974. *Phyton* **16**, Fasc. 1–4, 81–99.

Hawksworth, D. L. (1971). Lichens as litmus for air pollution: a historical review. *International Journal of Environmental Studies* **1**, 281–96.

Hawksworth, D. L. (1973) Mapping studies. In *Air pollution and lichens*, Eds B. W. Ferry, M. S. Baddeley & D. L. Hawksworth, pp. 38–76. Athlone Press, London.

Hawksworth, D. L. (1974). Literature on air pollution and lichens. *Lichenologist* **6**, 122–5.

Haywood, G. C., Hill, H. A. O., Pratt, J. M., Vanston, N. J. & Williams, R. J. P. (1965). The chemistry of vitamin B$_{12}$. IV. The thermodynamic trans effect. *Journal of the Chemical Society*, 6485–93.

Hill, D. J. (1971). Experimental study of the effect of sulphite on lichens with reference to atmospheric pollution. *New Phytologist* **70**, 831–6.

Hill, D. J. (1974). Some effects of sulphite on photosynthesis in lichens. *New Phytologist* **73**, 1193–1205.

Holt, A. S. (1958). The phase test intermediate and the allomerization of chlorphyll *a*. *Canadian Journal of Biochemistry and Physiology* **36**, 439–56.

Hynninen, P. H. & Assandri, S. (1973). Chlorophylls. II. Allomerization of chlorophylls *a* and *b*. *Acta Chemica Scandinavica* **27**, 1478–86.

Johnston, L. G. & Watson, W. F. (1956). The allomerization of chlorophyll. *Journal of the Chemical Society*, 1203–12.

LeBlanc, F. (1969). Epiphytes and air pollution. In *Air pollution. Proceedings of the first European congress on the influence of air pollution on animals and plants, 1968*, pp. 211–21. Centre for Agricultural Publishing and Documentation, Wageningen.

LeBlanc, F. & Rao, D. N. (1973). Effects of sulphur dioxide on lichen and moss transplants. *Ecology* **54**, 612–17.

Mabey, R. (1974). *The pollution handbook*. Penguin, London. 144 pp.

Mahler, H. R. & Cordes, E. H. (1966). *Biological chemistry*. Harper & Row, New York. 872 pp.

Margot, J. (1973). Experimental study of the effects of sulphur dioxide on the soredia of *Hypogymnia physodes*. In *Air pollution and lichens*, Eds B. W. Ferry, M. S. Baddeley & D. L. Hawksworth, pp. 314–29. Athlone Press, London.

Moore, C. C. (1974). A modification of the index of atmospheric purity method for substrate differences. *Lichenologist* **6**, 156–7.

Mukerji, S. K. & Yang, S. F. (1974). Phosphoenolpyruvate carboxylase from spinach leaf tissue. *Plant Physiology* **53**, 829–34.

Nash, T. H. (1973). Sensitivity of lichens to sulphur dioxide. *Bryologist* **76**, 333–9.

Nieboer, E., Puckett, K. J. & Grace, B. (1976). The uptake of nickel by *Umbilicaria muhlenbergii* (Ach.) Tuck: a physico–chemical process. *Canadian Journal of Botany*, in press.

Nylander, W. (1866). Les lichens du Jardin du Luxembourg. *Bulletin de la Société Botanique de France* **13**, 364–72.

Pearson. L. & Skye, E. (1965). Air pollution affects pattern of photosynthesis in *Parmelia sulcata*, a corticolous lichen. *Science* **148**, 1600–2.

Puckett, K. J. (1974). The ecology and physiology of lichens with respect to atmospheric pollution. PhD thesis, University of London. 313 pp.

Puckett, K. J., Nieboer, E., Flora, W. P. & Richardson, D. H. S. (1973). Sulphur dioxide: its effect on photosynthetic ^{14}C fixation in lichens and suggested mechanisms of phytotoxicity. *New Phytologist* **72**, 141–54.

Puckett, K. J., Richardson, D. H. S., Flora, W. P. & Nieboer, E. (1974). Photosynthetic ^{14}C fixation by the lichen *Umbilicaria muhlenbergii* (Ach.) Tuck: following short exposures to aqueous sulphur dioxide. *New Phytologist* **73**, 1183–92.

Rao, D. N. & LeBlanc, F. (1966). Effects of sulphur dioxide on the lichen algae with special reference to chlorophyll. *Bryologist* **69**, 69–75.

Richardson, D. H. S. (1975). *The vanishing lichens*. David & Charles, Newton Abbot, UK. 231 pp.

Richardson, D. H. S., Nieboer, E., Puckett, K. J., Grace, B. & Flora, W. P. (1974). *Potential sulphur dioxide damage to lichens of the MacKenzie Valley, N.W.T.* Interim Report to the Department of Atmospheric Environment Services, Environment Canada.

Richardson, D. H. S., Nieboer, E., Puckett, K. J., Grace, B. & Tomassini, F. D. (1975). *Potential sulphur dioxide damage to lichens of the MacKenzie Valley, N.W.T.* Final Report to the Department of Atmospheric Environment Services, Environment Canada.

Saunders, P. J. W. (1966). The toxicity of sulphur dioxide to *Diplocarpon rosae* Wolf. causing blackspot of roses. *Annals of Applied Biology* **58**, 103–14.

Scheer, H. & Katz, J. J. (1974). Structure of the Krasnovskii photoreduction product of chlorophyll *a*. *Proceedings of the National Academy of Sciences, USA* **71**, 1626–9.

Schiff, J. A. & Hodson, R. C. (1973). The metabolism of sulphate. *Annual Review of Plant Physiology* **24**, 381–414.

Seeley, G. R. (1966). The structure and chemistry of functional groups. In *The chlorophylls*, Eds L. P. Vernon & G. R. Seeley, pp. 67–109. Academic Press, New York & London.

Sernander, R. (1926). *Stockholm's nature*. Almquist & Wiksell, Uppsala.

Showman, R. E. (1972). Residual effects of sulphur dioxide on net photosynthesis and respiratory rates of lichen thalli and cultured lichen symbionts. *Bryologist* **75**, 335–41.

Sij, J. W. & Swanson, C. A. (1974). Short-term kinetic studies on the inhibition of photosynthesis by sulphur dioxide. *Journal of Environmental Quality* **3**, 103–7.

Sillén, L. G. & Martell, A. E. (1964). *Stability constants of metal-ion complexes.*

Chemical Society Special Publication No. 17. The Chemical Society, London.

Sillen, L. G. & Martell, A. E. (1971). *Stability constants of metal–ion complexes. Supplement No. 1. Chemical Society Special Publication No. 25.* The Chemical Society, London.

Syratt, W. J. & Wanstall, P. J. (1969). The effects of sulphur dioxide on epiphytic bryophytes. In *Air pollution. Proceedings of the first European congress on the influence of air pollution on animals and plants, 1968*, pp. 79–85. Centre for Agricultural Publishing and Research, Wageningen.

Tanaka, H., Takanashi, T. & Yatazawa, M. (1972a). Experimental studies on sulphur dioxide injuries in higher plants. I. Formation of glyoxylate bisulphite in plant leaves exposed to sulphur dioxide. *Water, Air and Soil Pollution* **1**, 205–11.

Tanaka, H., Takanashi, T., Kadota, M. & Yatazawa, M. (1972b). Experimental studies on sulphur dioxide injuries in higher plants. II. Disturbance of amino acid metabolism in plants exposed to sulphur dioxide. *Water, Air and Soil Pollution* **1**, 343–6.

Tanaka, H., Takanashi, T. & Yatazawa, M. (1974). Experimental studies on SO_2 injuries in higher plants. III. Inhibitory effect of sulfite ion on $^{14}CO_2$ fixation. *Water, Air and Soil Pollution* **3**, 11–16.

Tuominen, Y. & Jaakkola, T. (1973). Absorption and accumulation of mineral elements. In *The lichens*, Eds V. Ahmadjian & M. E. Hale, pp. 185–224. Academic Press, New York & London.

Türk, R., Wirth, V. & Lange, O. L. (1974). Carbon dioxide exchange measurements for determination of sulphur dioxide resistance of lichens. *Oecologia* **15**, 33–64.

Wellburn, A. R., Majernik, O. & Wellburn, F. A. M. (1972). Effects of SO_2 and NO_2 polluted air upon the ultrastructure of chloroplasts. *Environmental Pollution* **3**, 37–49.

Williams, R. J. P. (1973). Electron transfer and oxidative energy. *Biochemical Society Transactions* **1**, 1–26.

Ziegler, I. (1972). The effect of SO_3^{2-} on the activity of ribulose-1,5-diphosphate carboxylase in isolated spinach chloroplasts. *Planta* **103**, 155–63.

Ziegler, I. (1973). Effect of sulphite on phosphoenolpyruvate carboxylase and malate formation in extracts of *Zea mays*. *Phytochemistry* **12**, 1027–30.

Ziegler, I. (1974a). Action of sulphite on plant malate dehydrogenase. *Phytochemistry* **13**, 2411–16.

Ziegler, I. (1974b). Malate dehydrogenase in *Zea mays*: properties and inhibition by sulphite. *Biochimica et Biophysica Acta* **364**, 28–37.

J.N.B.BELL & C.H.MUDD

Sulphur dioxide resistance in plants: a case study of *Lolium perenne*

Evolution by plants of tolerance to pollutants is now well-documented. Particularly well-known examples are the natural evolution in several grass species of strains that are resistant to heavy metals in the substratum, and the success of the American tobacco growing industry in breeding ozone-tolerant strains of cigar-wrapper varieties to alleviate the serious pollution damage experienced in the eastern USA about fifteen years ago. In the case of sulphur dioxide (SO_2), many examples have been recorded of substantial intraspecific variation in tolerance to this pollutant (Tamm & Aronsson, 1972), and these

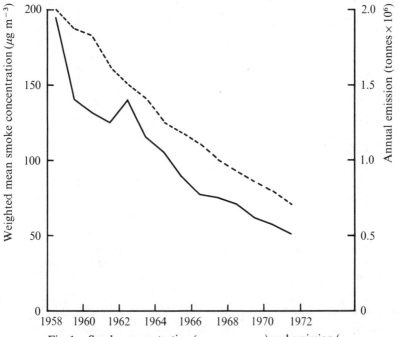

Fig. 1. Smoke concentration (————) and emission (– – – – – – –) trends in the United Kingdom. (Based on data from the Warren Spring Laboratory.)

probably account for some of the discrepancies found by different workers when determining threshold levels for injury and relative susceptibility of plant species. However, in most cases the possession of tolerance to sulphur dioxide has not been related to environmental conditions prevailing in the field, but such an example is described in this paper.

During the last twenty years, major changes have taken place in the characteristics of sulphur dioxide pollution in the United Kingdom. Following the introduction of the Clean Air Act of 1956, there has been a steady decline in the smoke in suspension in the atmosphere, largely in response to the reduction in coal-burning by low-level sources such as domestic fires (Fig. 1). At the same time, although there has been no corresponding decrease in sulphur dioxide emissions over the country as a whole, concentrations in urban areas have declined (Fig. 2) as more smoke control areas have been

Fig. 2.   Sulphur dioxide emission (– – – – – – – –) and urban concentration (————) trends in the United Kingdom. (Based on data from the Warren Spring Laboratory and redrawn from Anon., 1974.)

established, but it has been suggested that this may be partly the result of changed meteorological conditions, with a reduced frequency of stagnant weather in winter (Chamberlain & Penkett, 1972). Information on concentrations in rural areas is limited, because very few of the National Survey of

Air Pollution sampling stations are situated outside towns, these being established primarily for the purpose of monitoring concentrations potentially hazardous to human health. However, there is some evidence that rural concentrations are as high as ever and possibly increasing. Fig. 3 shows the mean winter sulphur dioxide concentrations at urban and rural sites respectively over recent years in the North-West Region of the National Survey of Air Pollution. This region contains many industrial districts,

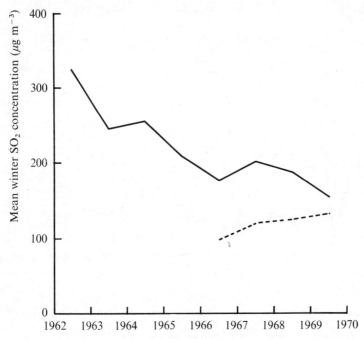

Fig. 3.   Trends in mean winter sulphur dioxide concentrations at urban (————————) and rural (– – – – – – – –) sites in the North-West Region of the National Survey of Air Pollution. (Based on data from the Warren Spring Laboratory and redrawn from Anon., 1972.)

including the cities of Manchester and Liverpool, but possesses a number of sampling stations which are situated outside towns in rural areas. The sulphur dioxide levels at the urban sites show a progressive fall, but the concentrations at the rural stations have risen until they are almost the same as in the towns. The reason for this situation can probably be sought in the changing pattern of industry, with increasing emissions from tall chimneys, particularly at power-stations, which result in a greater dispersion of flue-gases over the countryside.

Air pollution injury and field trials at Helmshore

Obvious visible injury to crops by sulphur dioxide pollution is rare in rural areas of the United Kingdom. However, in the Rossendale hill-farming district of east Lancashire, which is within the North-West Region of the National Survey of Air Pollution, it has been recorded on many occasions. This is a district in which the sulphur dioxide levels in winter are generally high (Fig. 4) and have probably been so since the appearance of coal-smoke

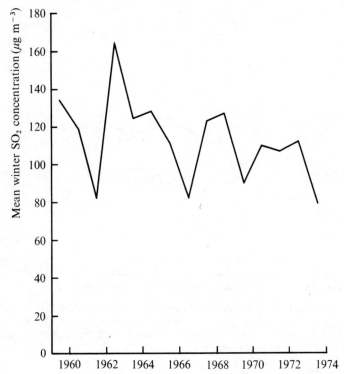

Fig. 4.   Mean winter (October–March inclusive) sulphur dioxide concentration trends at Helmshore. (Based on data from the Warren Spring Laboratory and Great House Experimental Husbandry Farm, Helmshore.)

pollution during the Industrial Revolution, early in the last century. The Rossendale area consists of steep-sided valleys, with small industrial towns situated in the bottom and grasslands on the sides, giving way to moorland on the surrounding plateaux.

The practice of re-seeding grassland, i.e. the replacement of indigenous species with improved species and varieties, became widespread during and after the Second World War in an attempt to increase productivity. In some cases the results were disappointing and reversion to the original species often occurred. This was due in part to a failure to provide the high level of fertility required by the sown species, but in the industrial southern Pennines, which includes the Rossendale area, there was strong circumstantial evidence that the failure of the introduced species was the result of atmospheric pollution. Observations and field trials have been carried out into this situation over the last 24 years at the Agricultural Development and Advisory Service's Great House Experimental Husbandry Farm, which is situated at Helmshore in the Rossendale Pennines, about fifteen miles north of Manchester. At Helmshore air pollution damage has appeared on many occasions on sown grass species, including both chronic injury, characterised by a yellowing of the leaves, and acute injury which usually consists of white necroses on the leaves. The commercially important S23 and S24 varieties of *Lolium perenne* L. (perennial ryegrass) proved particularly susceptible and after introduction into the Helmshore area became eliminated due to damage in the winter months when resistance was low and pollution levels were high. In contrast the indigenous grasses, including *Lolium perenne*, appeared to be resistant to the prevailing levels of air pollution in the vicinity.

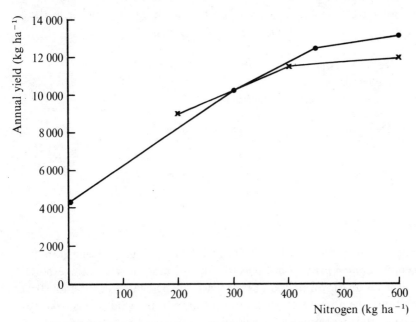

Fig. 5.   Response to nitrogen of swards containing S23 (×————×) and indigenous (•————•) *Lolium perenne* at Helmshore.

Work at Helmshore has concentrated upon the encouragement of these indigenous grass types, particularly *Lolium perenne*, because it has been shown that, given the right management, the indigenous ryegrass is as productive as the commercially bred varieties (Fig. 5). Large additions of nitrogen have overcome many of the earlier problems with air pollution at Helmshore, but there is still a tendency for S23 swards to deteriorate and the indigenous swards to improve with time. A number of clones of indigenous ryegrass were selected for productivity and resistance to the local pollution, but there has been little response from commercial firms to market the seed from these strains.

A transplant experiment was carried out to examine the performance at Helmshore of indigenous ryegrass collected from an unpolluted area, situated 3 km from the Fylde coast near Blackpool. Clones of indigenous ryegrass from both the Fylde and Helmshore were potted in the same soil and grown outside at both sites. Near the coast there is some deposition of salt, but pollutant levels are low. On the other hand at Helmshore salt is rarely detected, because the site is 50 km from the coast, but there is a fairly high level of sulphur dioxide from the neighbouring towns. Coastal ryegrass showed stunting and severe, acute injury at Helmshore and the Helmshore ryegrass showed damage from salt spray near the coasts, and in both cases a substantial decline in productivity took place early in the second growing season after transplantation (Table 1). In contrast when growing in their own native environments, both types were undamaged.

Table 1.   *Dry weight (g per pot) of indigenous Helmshore and Fylde* Lolium perenne *at first cut following the year of establishment*

Site of origin	Site of experiment	
	Helmshore	Fylde
Helmshore	83.9	55.1
Fylde	68.3	105.9

S.E.M. = 14.6.

Thus there is some indication from this field trial that at Helmshore the indigenous *Lolium perenne* has selected for resistance to coal-smoke pollution, over an unknown period of time since the beginning of the Industrial Revolution. The absence of pollution resistance in the wild plants from the coast lends further support for this idea, as opposed to the possibility of susceptibility having been bred into the commercial varieties, which were originally developed at Aberystwyth in an area where pollutant levels are very low.

Growth experiments in fumigation chambers

Although the work at Helmshore suggests that the indigenous ryegrass has evolved tolerance to the local air pollution, it does not show which pollutant is responsible, although sulphur dioxide is strongly implicated. Also the field trials had no true controls: ideally plants should also have been grown in clean air so that a comparison could be obtained between growth in polluted and non-polluted conditions. Accordingly a series of experiments was performed at Imperial College, under more controlled conditions, into the magnitude and nature of this tolerance.

Initially two experiments were carried out in which Helmshore and S23 ryegrass were grown at realistic concentrations of sulphur dioxide for relatively long periods (Bell & Clough, 1973). The experiments were conducted in a pair of Perspex chambers, situated outdoors. These are ventilated with the ambient air which is first purified of gaseous pollutants by passage through activated charcoal, followed by elimination of particulates with an absolute filter. One chamber is ventilated only with this clean air to act as a control, while the other is ventilated with the same air into which sulphur dioxide is released from a cylinder to give a controlled low concentration. The chamber inlets point upwards and a satisfactory distribution of the gas around the chambers is achieved. The chambers are unheated so that conditions in them approximate to the ambient for much of the time, although some problems are experienced with heating in summer. The sulphur dioxide concentration in each chamber was monitored over weekly intervals throughout the course of each experiment by bubbling air through hydrogen peroxide which was later analysed for its sulphate content.

The first experiment was carried out during the summer with a mean sulphur dioxide concentration of 343 μg m^{-3} in the polluted chamber. This is high for a mean concentration in the field, being fairly typical of the levels experienced in industrial towns in winter. In each chamber six bowls containing a fertilised brown earth were planted with sixteen uniform tillers from two clones of indigenous Helmshore ryegrass. In another nine bowls per chamber the same soil was sown with the commercial S23 strain of *L. perenne*, which field observations at Helmshore had indicated was susceptible to coal-smoke pollution. The plants were grown for nine weeks and then harvested. At the time of harvesting the S23 plants which had been grown in the polluted chamber were visibly smaller and chlorotic in comparison with the controls. On the other hand the indigenous Helmshore plants were a healthy green colour in both the polluted and the clean-air chambers.

When the plants were harvested, it was found that a reduction of 41% in shoot dry weight of the S23 plants had taken place in the polluted chamber compared with the controls (Table 2). In contrast the sulphur dioxide had

Table 2.   *Shoot dry weights (g) of S23 and Helmshore* Lolium perenne *plants grown for 9 weeks in 343* $\mu g\ m^{-3}$ *or 14* $\mu g\ m^{-3}$ SO_2

	Polluted chamber (343 $\mu g\ m^{-3}\ SO_2$)	Control chamber (14 $\mu g\ m^{-3}\ SO_2$)	P
S23	0.298 ±0.024	0.502 ±0.019	< 0.001
Helmshore	0.535 ±0.075	0.544 ±0.065	Not significant

Values show means per plant ±S.E.M.

produced no effect on the yield of the indigenous Helmshore plants, there being no significant difference between the clean and polluted air.

Because there had been no replication of gas treatments, the second experiment was performed with the roles of the chambers reversed, so that the former polluted chamber was now the control chamber and vice versa. This time the experiment was carried out for a period of 26 weeks over winter with a mean sulphur dioxide concentration of 191 $\mu g\ m^{-3}$, this being of the same order as the levels experienced over some years at Helmshore. Again both types of ryegrass were grown, with two similar clones of Helmshore plants being used. This time at the end of the experiment the shoot dry weight

Table 3.   *Shoot dry weights (g) of S23 and Helmshore* Lolium perenne *plants grown for 26 weeks in 191* $\mu g\ m^{-3}$ *or 9* $\mu g\ m^{-3}$ SO_2

	Polluted chamber (191 $\mu g\ m^{-3}\ SO_2$)	Control chamber (9 $\mu g\ m^{-3}\ SO_2$)	P
S23	0.653 ±0.036	1.296 ±0.040	< 0.001
Helmshore	1.377 ±0.037	1.388 ±0.027	Not significant

Values shown are mean per plant ±S.E.M.

of the S23 plants was depressed in sulphur dioxide by 50% in comparison with the controls, but again the Helmshore plants showed the same productivity in each chamber (Table 3).

Both types of ryegrass had the same visual appearance as at the end of the first experiment, the S23 plants being chlorotic and the Helmshore plants having a healthy green appearance when grown in sulphur dioxide.

Clean-air field trial

It was not possible to make a direct comparison of growth between S23 and Helmshore plants within either of the chambers, because the former had been grown from seed and the latter from tillers. It was considered possible that the difference in response to sulphur dioxide might be based on differential growth rates in the two ryegrass types: a fast-growing plant might be affected to a greater or lesser extent than one whose increase in dry matter was slower. The previous evidence from Helmshore shows that the indigenous ryegrass is capable of showing productivity as high as the S23 variety in the field under suitable conditions. However, the Helmshore district has relatively high levels of air pollution and it was decided to compare the growth of the two types over a period of several years at a site with fairly clean air. Accordingly a field trial was laid out in the autumn of 1972 at the Imperial College Field Station, near Ascot, Berkshire. This consisted of a high and low level of soil fertility, the two ryegrass types, and five replicates randomised in a complete factorial design. The plants were grown as swards in 1.4 m × 1.4 m squares, with S23 seed sown at a rate of 30 kg ha^{-1} and Helmshore tillers from a single clone planted at 10-cm intervals.

Samples of 1 m^2 from the swards were harvested throughout the summer at intervals of 34 to 40 days by cutting down to 5 cm above ground level and then allowing regrowth; the dry weight of harvested material was then obtained. During the summer of 1973 four harvests were made, but in the summer of 1974 when the plants were better established this was increased to five harvests. Table 4 shows that the high fertiliser treatment significantly increased total yields in nearly all cases. In 1973 there was a significant variety/fertiliser interaction, with no difference between the two varieties at high fertility, but with the S23 plants showing a higher productivity than the Helmshore plants at the low fertility level. In 1974 the analysis of variance showed that overall, S23 was more productive than the Helmshore ryegrass: there was, however, no significant interaction, although there was still an indication that S23 was significantly more productive, mainly at low fertility. Thus over a 2-year period at a high fertility level the growth rates of the

Table 4.   *Total annual shoot dry matter production* $(kg^{-1} ha^{-1} yr^{-1} \pm$ S.E.M.) *of S23 and Helmshore* Lolium perenne *at two fertility levels*

	1973			1974		
	S23	Helmshore	P	S23	Helmshore	P
High fertility	7990 ± 660	8700 ± 510	Not significant	10 370 ± 250	9630 ± 350	Not significant
Low fertility	6790 ± 270	4810 ± 490	0.01 –0.001	6540 ± 460	5490 ± 250	0.05 –0.1
P	Not significant	< 0.001		< 0.001	< 0.001	

Helmshore and S23 ryegrass types do not significantly differ. In the chamber experiments a high fertility soil was employed and thus it seems that inherent differences in growth rates do not explain the tolerance to sulphur dioxide of the indigenous Helmshore ryegrass. In 1974 the productivity of the Helmshore and S23 ryegrass types compared favourably with the published figure of about $10\,000\ kg\ ha^{-1}\ yr^{-1}$ for commercial varieties grown in fertile lowland soil with fairly infrequent cutting (Spedding & Diekmahns, 1972).

Physiological experiments

Recently a series of investigations into the physiological basis of the differences between the Helmshore and S23 ryegrass types has been started.

Sulphur content of plants

Total sulphur content of the leaf blades was measured in both ryegrass types in the two gas treatments at the termination of both fumigation experiments

Table 5.   *Sulphur content (ppm dry weight* $\pm$ S.E.M.) *of living leaf blades after:*

(a) 9 weeks at 343 µg m^{-3} or 14 µg m^{-3} SO$_2$		(b) 26 weeks at 191 µg m^{-3} or 9 µg m^{-3} SO$_2$	
S23		S23	
14 µg m^{-3} SO$_2$ (control)	3714 $\pm$ 201	9 µg m^{-3} SO$_2$ (control)	3984 $\pm$ 186
343 µg m^{-3} SO$_2$	7260 $\pm$ 417	191 µg m^{-3} SO$_2$	7583 $\pm$ 422
Helmshore		Helmshore	
14 µg m^{-3} SO$_2$ (control)	3653 $\pm$ 255	9 µg m^{-3} SO$_2$ (control)	3833 $\pm$ 183
343 µg m^{-3} SO$_2$	7965 $\pm$ 266	191 µg m^{-3} SO$_2$	5732 $\pm$ 230

(Table 5). In the case of the S23 plants the sulphur concentration of the fumigated plants was approximately twice that of the S23 controls in both experiments. In the 343 μg m^{-3} experiment the Helmshore plants showed similar levels of sulphur to the S23 plants in each treatment; however, in the 191 μg m^{-3} experiment when different clones of Helmshore plants were used, these contained a significantly lower concentration of sulphur than the S23 plants when both had been grown in the sulphur dioxide chamber. At first sight this suggests that at least some Helmshore plants possess a mechanism for reducing uptake of sulphur dioxide. However, when the total uptake of atmospheric sulphur per plant was calculated (Table 6), it

Table 6. *Uptake of atmospheric sulphur (mg per plant) by S23 and Helmshore* Lolium perenne *plants in fumigation experiments*

9 weeks at 343 μg m^{-3} or 14 μg m^{-3} SO$_2$		26 weeks at 191 μg m^{-3} or 9 μg m^{-3} SO$_2$	
Helmshore	1.64 mg	Helmshore	1.69 mg
S23	0.77 mg	S23	1.57 mg

was found that this was smaller in the S23 than in the Helmshore plants. Thus there is evidence that the tolerance in the indigenous Helmshore plants is not due to exclusion of sulphur dioxide from either individual leaves or from the sward as a whole.

Stomatal characteristics

Dean (1972) and Menser, Hodges & McKee (1973) have shown that some ozone-sensitive tobacco varieties possess a higher stomatal frequency than resistant varieties. Accordingly stomatal counts were made of unit areas of the leaves of S23 and Helmshore ryegrass plants and measurements also obtained of their stomatal lengths (Table 7), but no significant differences were found between the two types. Ting & Dugger (1971) and Turner, Rich

Table 7. *Stomatal characteristics of S23 and Helmshore* Lolium perenne *($\pm$ s.e.m.)*

Stomatal characteristic	Helmshore	S23	P
Stomatal frequency (no. per field)	38.3 $\pm$ 1.2	39.3 $\pm$ 1.7	N.S.*
Stomatal length (μm)	23.4 $\pm$ 0.9	22.8 $\pm$ 0.9	N.S.
Stomatal resistance (s cm^{-1})	2.91 $\pm$ 0.24	2.55 $\pm$ 0.23	N.S.

* Not significant.

& Tomlinson (1972) have demonstrated that ozone-tolerant tobacco varieties have an inherently higher stomatal resistance than sensitive cultivars. The two ryegrass types were thus investigated with respect to their stomatal resistances. Helmshore and S23 plants were placed in a growth cabinet, adjusted to give a regime of a 13-h day with 250 μE m^{-2} s^{-1} photosynthetically active radiation (PAR), and temperatures of 21 °C by day and 15 °C by night. Selected leaves of similar age on each plant were carefully fixed at 90° to the incident radiation and the stomatal resistances of these were then estimated by means of a Lambda diffusive resistance porometer. No significant differences could be found between the stomatal resistances of the two ryegrass types, and this was confirmed by repeating the experiment both in the growth cabinet and in a greenhouse. Thus it seems that the tolerance of the indigenous Helmshore ryegrass is not explained by an inherently greater stomatal resistance than the S23 variety.

Majernik & Mansfield (1970) and Biscoe, Unsworth & Pinckney (1973) have shown increased opening of the stomata of *Vicia faba* in the presence of sulphur dioxide. However, in both cases these effects were only demonstrated with short fumigation periods and it is not known whether they have relevance to the long-term situation in the field, where stomata might adapt to the continued presence of sulphur dioxide. In fact Cowling, Jones & Lockyer (1973) showed no increase in transpiration of S23 *Lolium perenne* plants after a 59-day fumigation with 131 μg m^{-3} sulphur dioxide compared with plants grown in clean air. It was considered possible that differences in stomatal response to sulphur dioxide might be involved in the mechanism of differential susceptibility of the two types of ryegrass. S23 and indigenous Helmshore plants were grown for 129 days over winter in outdoor fumigation chambers in clean air or in an atmosphere containing 150 μg m^{-3} sulphur dioxide. The stomatal resistances of five plants of each type from each gas treatment were measured between 11.30 and 13.30 h on a day when the temperature in the chambers was 7.5 °C, the relative humidity was 94%, and PAR averaged 110 μE m^{-2} s^{-1}, but no significant differences were found (Table 8). Although it is necessary for these measurements to be repeated under different environmental conditions, this work suggests that sulphur dioxide does not have a long-term effect on the stomatal resistances of either S23 or Helmshore *L. perenne*. Another preliminary experiment examined the effects on the stomatal resistance of the two ryegrass types of a two hour high concentration fumigation, such as might be experienced in an acute injury situation in the field at Helmshore, but again there was no evidence of any differential response.

The available information implies that the resistance of the indigenous Helmshore *L. perenne* is not the result of an avoidance mechanism by which

Table 8.   *Stomatal resistances (s cm^{-1} ±*S.E.M.*) of S23 and* Helmshore Lolium perenne *after exposure to 150 μg m^{-3} sulphur dioxide or clean air for 129 days*

	150 μg m^{-3} SO$_2$	Control	P
Helmshore	12.13±0.58	14.89±3.85	N.S.*
S23	11.70±0.75	13.45±1.98	N.S.
P	N.S.	N.S.	

* Not significant.

the plant physically prevents sulphur dioxide from entering the leaf. Thus the basis of the resistance mechanism must be sought in effects on some fundamental physiological process within the plant.

Effects on chlorophylls

High concentrations of sulphur dioxide have been shown to cause the degradation of chlorophylls to phaeophytins (Rao & LeBlanc, 1966; Coker,

Table 9.   *Chlorophyll content (μg cm^{-2}) of* Lolium perenne *leaves after 26 weeks in 191 μg m^{-3} or 9 μg m^{-3} SO$_2$*

(a) S23

	Chlorophyll a	Chlorophyll b	Total chlorophyll	Ratio a:b
191 μg m^{-3} SO$_2$	18.45 ±1.22	6.68 ±0.38	25.32 ±1.56	2.69 ±0.09
9 μg m^{-3} SO$_2$ (control)	24.12 ±1.88	9.21 ±0.60	33.33 ±2.45	2.61 ±0.07
P	0.02–0.05	0.01–0.001	0.01–0.02	N.S.*

(b) Helmshore

	Chlorophyll a	Chlorophyll b	Total chlorophyll	Ratio a:b
191 μg m^{-3} SO$_2$	23.37 ±1.63	8.67 ±0.52	32.05 ±2.09	2.70 ±0.10
9 μg m^{-3} SO$_2$ (control)	21.75 ±3.26	9.26 ±1.56	31.01 ±4.74	2.39 ±0.17
P	N.S.	N.S.	N.S.	N.S.

Values show means ±S.E.M.

* Not significant.

1967), but there is substantial evidence that this effect does not occur *in vivo* with realistic concentrations of the gas (Arndt, 1971). Williams, Lloyd & Ricks (1971) have shown that in *Quercus petraea* growing in a sulphur dioxide polluted woodland, an abnormally greater degradation of chlorophyll *a* than chlorophyll *b* occurred as the growing season progressed. In the present investigation the concentrations of chlorophylls *a* and *b* were measured in S23 and Helmshore plants which had been fumigated for 26 weeks in 191 μg m^{-3} sulphur dioxide or clean air (9 μg m^{-3} SO$_2$) (Table 9). When grown in sulphur dioxide, amounts of chlorophylls *a* and *b* in the S23 plants were reduced by 23.5% and 25.5% respectively compared with the clean-air controls. In comparison the indigenous Helmshore plants showed no significant differences in their chlorophyll concentrations between the two gas treatments. Thus it would seem that the Helmshore plants, in contrast to the S23 variety, possess some mechanism which prevents sulphur dioxide from affecting the rates of synthesis or degradation of chlorophylls. However, the significance of the reduced chlorophyll content in the S23 plants in relation to the observed depression in yield remains to be assessed: unless chlorophyll concentration was limiting photosynthesis during early stages of growth under the experimental conditions it may have had no adverse result and may merely have been a secondary manifestation of chronic sulphur dioxide injury.

Effects on membranes

The possibility of a realistic concentration of sulphur dioxide producing a differential response in membrane permeability between the S23 and Helmshore ryegrass types was investigated. Segments 2.5 cm long from leaves of uniform age were removed from plants which had been subjected to 140 μg m^{-3} sulphur dioxide or clean air for 81 days during the winter. The ends of the segments were sealed with petroleum jelly and these were then submerged in 2 ml of distilled water for 30 min. The potassium concentration of the distilled water was determined by flame photometry and then the total potassium content of the segments estimated after the addition of more water, following drying at 105 °C to destroy all the membranes. The percentage of the total potassium which leaked out of the living leaf after 30 min submersion was taken as an index of membrane permeability. Table 10 shows that there were no significant differences in membrane permeability between the plant types or gas treatments and so this can be discounted so far as levels of sulphur dioxide which produce chronic injury are concerned. Further work has investigated the effects of short bursts of concentrations of sulphur dioxide which are high enough to result in acute injury; there is some indication that the membranes of Helmshore plants have a lower potassium leakage

Table 10.   *Leakage of potassium (% of total ±S.E.M.) from S23 and Helmshore* Lolium perenne *after exposure to 140 µg m^{-3} SO$_2$ or clean air for 81 days*

	140 µg m^{-3} SO$_2$	Control	P
Helmshore	1.38 ± 0.07	1.94 ± 0.42	N.S.*
S23	1.30 ± 0.17	1.37 ± 0.17	N.S.
P	N.S.	N.S.	

* Not significant.

rate than S23 plants in these circumstances, but the differences have not proved to be statistically significant because of substantial variation between replicates.

Summary

Observations at Helmshore in a region of Lancashire with a long history of coal-smoke pollution, have shown that the commercial S23 strain of *Lolium perenne* is adversely affected by the prevailing levels of atmospheric pollutants. In contrast, the indigenous ryegrass appears to have evolved resistance to coal-smoke pollution, but the time scale during which this has taken place is unknown. Fumigation experiments have shown that a sulphur dioxide concentration characteristic of the mean winter level in the Helmshore area suppresses yield substantially in S23 ryegrass but has no effect on clones of the indigenous *L. perenne*. A field trial has indicated that the differences in resistance between the two types of ryegrass cannot be explained on the basis of differential growth rates. Further investigations have shown that the resistance mechanism is not based on a reduction of penetration of sulphur dioxide into the leaf due to differences in stomatal resistances and response. This indicates that the mechanism must be connected with some physiological process inside the plant. A sulphur dioxide level which reduced the concentration of chlorophylls *a* and *b* in S23 ryegrass had no effect on the concentration of either of these pigments in the indigenous Helmshore plants. It is considered that the differential response to sulphur dioxide of chlorophyll synthesis or degradation may be an important factor in the resistance mechanism. Many more physiological aspects of the problem remain to be investigated, particularly the effects of sulphur dioxide on photosynthesis and respiration, rates of oxidation of sulphite to sulphate within the plant, and metabolic pathways of atmospherically derived sulphur in the two ryegrass types.

The earlier fumigation experiments on the effects of sulphur dioxide on growth were performed in conjunction with Dr W. S. Clough and were sponsored by the Atomic Energy Research Establishment, Harwell. We thank Miss J. Relton and Mr M. Alcock for assistance with the physiological experiments and Professor A. J. Rutter and Dr J. W. Hannay for their constructive criticism of the manuscript.

References

Anon. (1972). *National survey of air pollution 1961–1971. Vol. 2, South West Region, North Wales Region, North West Region.* London, Her Majesty's Stationery Office.

Anon. (1974). *Clean air today.* London, Her Majesty's Stationery Office.

Arndt, U. (1971). Konzentrationsanderungen bei Blattfarbstoffen unter dem Einfluss von Luftverunreinigungen. Ein Diskussionsbeitrag zur Pigmentanalyse. *Environmental Pollution* 2, 37–48.

Bell, J. N. B. & Clough, W. S. (1973). Depression of yield in ryegrass exposed to sulphur dioxide. *Nature, London* 241, 47–9.

Biscoe, P. V., Unsworth, M. H. & Pinckney, H. R. (1973). The effects of low concentrations of sulphur dioxide on stomatal behaviour in *Vicia faba*. *New Phytologist* 72, 1299–1306.

Chamberlain, A. C. & Penkett, S. A. (1972). Atmospheric pollution – present trends and future problems. *Contemporary Physics* 13, 179–98.

Coker, P. D. (1967). Effects of sulphur dioxide on bark epiphytes. *Transactions of the British Bryological Society* 5, 341–7.

Cowling, D. W., Jones, L. H. P. & Lockyer, D. R. (1973). Increased yields through correction of sulphur deficiency in ryegrass exposed to sulphur dioxide. *Nature, London* 243, 479–80.

Dean, C. E. (1972). Stomate density and size as related to ozone-induced weather fleck in tobacco. *Crop Science* 12, 547–8.

Majernik, O. & Mansfield, T. A. (1970). Direct effect of SO_2 pollution on the degree of opening of stomata. *Nature, London* 227, 377–8.

Menser, H. A., Hodges, G. H. & McKee, C. G. (1973). Effects of air pollution on Maryland (Type 32) tobacco. *Journal of Environmental Quality* 2, 253–8.

Rao, D. N. & LeBlanc, F. (1966). Effects of SO_2 on the lichen alga with special reference to chlorophyll. *Bryologist* 69, 69–75.

Spedding, C. R. W. & Diekmahns, E. C. (1972). *Grasses and legumes in British agriculture*, p. 154. Commonwealth Agricultural Bureau, Farnham Royal, UK.

Tamm, C. O. & Aronsson, A. (1972). *Plant growth as affected by sulphur compounds in a polluted atmosphere. Literature survey No. 12.* Department of Forest Ecology and Forest Soils, College of Forestry, Stockholm.

Ting, I. P. & Dugger, W. M. (1971). Ozone resistance in tobacco plants: a possible relationship to water balance. *Atmospheric Environment* 5, 147–50.

Turner, N. C., Rich, S. & Tomlinson, H. (1972). Stomatal conductance, fleck injury, and growth of tobacco cultivars ranging in ozone tolerance. *Phytopathology* **62**, 63–7.

Williams, R. J. H., Lloyd, M. M. & Ricks, G. R. (1971). Effects of atmospheric pollution on deciduous woodland. I. Some effects on leaves of *Quercus petraea* (Mattuschka) Leibl. *Environmental Pollution* **2**, 57–68.

A.R.WELLBURN, T.M.CAPRON, H.-S.CHAN & D.C.HORSMAN

Biochemical effects of atmospheric pollutants on plants

The earlier work of the Lancaster group on the effects of sulphur dioxide (SO_2) upon stomatal opening (Majernik & Mansfield, 1970, 1971; Mansfield & Majernik, 1970) and that of sulphur dioxide and nitrogen dioxide (NO_2) on chloroplast ultrastructure (Wellburn, Majernik & Wellburn, 1972) has stimulated biochemical studies on plants in polluted environments. These have been accompanied by parallel physiological investigations (e.g. Bull & Mansfield, 1974) and particular attention has been paid to identifying those biochemical mechanisms in plants which are immediately affected by the presence of air pollutants. There have been many investigations reported in the literature to identify changed cellular conditions in response to particular air pollutants. In Appendix II to this volume we have summarised the most important known metabolic effects of some of the more common air pollutants, paying particular attention to changes in levels of enzymic activity. The rationale for choosing levels of enzyme activities as evidence of changed cellular conditions has also been covered earlier in this volume by Nieboer *et al.*

Methods and materials

Fumigation

Seedlings of *Pisum sativum L.* (var. Feltham First) and *Lycopersicon esculentum* Mill. (var. Moneymaker) were grown and fumigated in essentially the same manner as described elsewhere (Horsman & Wellburn, 1975). Seedlings of *Rumex obtusifolius*, grown from seeds collected in the close vicinity of the Widnes 1 and Thornton Cleveleys 2 monitoring sites of the National Survey of Smoke and Sulphur Dioxide (Department of Trade and Industry, Warren Spring Laboratory), were fumigated in a wind tunnel apparatus operating at 25 changes min^{-1} of either clean air or clean air polluted with 0.2 ppm sulphur dioxide.

Pollutants were generated from special gas mixtures supplied by the British Oxygen Company and the oxides of nitrogen and sulphur dioxide were measured as before (Horsman & Wellburn, 1975; Capron & Mansfield, 1975). Levels of ammonia (NH_3) were measured using the method of Weatherburn (1967) and propylene was estimated using a Pye Unicam 104 gas–liquid chromatogram employing a 2.5-m column of silica, with an argon flow rate of 200 cm^3 min^{-1} and a temperature of 100 °C.

Enzyme assays

The maceration and enzyme assay systems employed for the work on tomato (*Lycopersicon*) seedlings were essentially those reported earlier (Horsman & Wellburn, 1975) with the addition of nitrite reductase assays essentially as described by Racker (1963).

The assays on pea (*Pisum*) and dock (*Rumex*) seedlings were the same as before but ethylenediamine tetra-acetic acid and reduced glutathione were omitted from the grinding medium and 2.5 mM cysteine incorporated instead. The methods for assay of glutamate dehydrogenase and of glutamine synthetase were those of Pahlich & Joy (1971) and Pahlich, Jäger & Steubing (1972) respectively, and the method of Haydar & Hadziyev (1973) was used to estimate lipoxidase activities.

All activities were calculated on the basis of either total soluble protein, chlorophyll, fresh weight, dry weight and per seedling (see Horsman & Wellburn, 1975). Each basis of expression was tested for independent change during fumigation. Total soluble protein was found to give the least bias to the expression of enzyme activity and was employed for the calculation of percentage change of activity from simultaneous controls. This is the most useful method of expressing results of this type and is used throughout.

Results

Effects of single pollutants such as sulphur dioxide, nitrogen dioxide, ammonia or nitric oxide on peas and tomatoes

Most experimental fumigations involve a single pollutant, although this is rarely the prevailing situation in urban and industrial environments. The results shown in Table 1 are the accumulation of initial studies employing single pollutants where originally the main object was to identify suitable enzymes for more detailed biochemical studies (which are still in progress), or before carrying out further experiments involving two or more pollutants.

Table 1 shows that the levels of glutamate dehydrogenase (GDH) and glutamate pyruvate transaminase (GPT) activity are on the whole stimulated

Table 1. *Significant* changes in enzyme levels when 2-week-old pea* (Pisum) *and 6-week-old tomato* (Lycopersicon) *seedlings are polluted with a single pollutant for 6 days and 3 weeks respectively*

Seedling	Pisum							Lycopersicon		
Pollutant	SO_2			NH_3	NO_2			NO_2		NO
Concentration (ppm)	0.5	1.0	2.0	0.5	0.1	0.2	1.0	0.1	0.5	0.4
Glutamate oxaloacetate transaminase (GOT)	...	↑	↑	...	↓	...	—	↓	↓	↓
Glutamate pyruvate transaminase (GPT)	—	↑	↑	—	—	—	—	↑	—	—
Glutamate dehydrogenase (GDH)	↑	...	...	↑	—	↑	...	...	...	...
Glutamine synthetase (GS)	—	...	...	—	—	—	...	...	...	...
Peroxidase	↑	↑	↑	↑	—	—	—	↓	↓	↑
Nitrite reductase	...	...	...	...	...	...	...	—	—	↑
Ribulose-1,5-diphosphate carboxylase (RuDPC)	—	—	↓	—	—	—	↑	↓	↑	↑
Lipoxidase	—	...	...	—	—	—	...	...	...	...

(↑) stimulation or (↓) inhibition at $P < 0.05$ or less; — no effect ($P > 0.05$); ... not assayed.

* As determined by comparison of the relevant t statistic.

by sulphur dioxide and nitrogen dioxide whereas the levels of peroxidase, ribulose-1,5-diphosphate carboxylase (RuDPC) and glutamate oxaloacetate transaminase (GOT) activity are more variable. On the other hand glutamine synthetase (GS) and lipoxidase are relatively unaffected by these pollutants.

Effects of sulphur dioxide plus nitrogen dioxide on pea seedlings

Monitoring studies of industrial pollution on the Heysham peninsula have shown the mixed presence of sulphur dioxide and nitrogen dioxide. A preliminary report of the physiological effect of a mixture of these two gases upon vegetation (Bull & Mansfield, 1974) has shown that under laboratory conditions they may produce an additive inhibition of net photosynthesis in pea seedlings. A parallel enzyme study using many different enzymes has been reported elsewhere in detail (Horsman & Wellburn, 1975) but results at a lower range of concentrations and including estimates of GDH activities have subsequently been obtained. These later results for GDH activities and the overall analyses of variance to test for the effects of sulphur dioxide, nitrogen dioxide and a mixture of the two are shown in Tables 2 and 3 respectively.

Table 2 shows that GDH activity is stimulated quite markedly in this 5×3

Table 2. *Changes in glutamate dehydrogenase (GDH) activity in 14-day-old pea seedlings fumigated for the final 6 days with different levels of SO_2 and NO_2*

NO₂ (ppm)	SO₂ (ppm)				
	0	0.1	0.2	0.3	0.5
0	100	103	100	109	137
0.1	100	100	107	115	142
0.2	105	102	125	139	170

Values expressed as % of unpolluted controls.

Table 3. *F values and significance levels from a 5 × 3 factorial experiment to test for SO_2, NO_2 and $SO_2 + NO_2$ effects on enzymic activities of pea seedlings*

Enzyme	SO₂[a]	NO₂[b]	SO₂[a] + NO₂[b]
Ribulose-1,5-diphosphate carboxylase (RuDPC)	3.28*(↓)	0.20	1.59
Peroxidase	9.79***(↑)	2.80	2.85*(↑)
Glutamate pyruvate transaminase (GPT)	4.88**(↑)	2.62	4.92**(↑)
Glutamate dehydrogenase (GDH)	68.40***(↑)	1.18	28.66***(↑)
Glutamine synthetase (GS)	2.13	1.18	2.43

[a] 0, 0.1, 0.2, 0.3 and 0.5 ppm SO₂.

[b] 0, 0.1 and 0.2 ppm NO₂.

* $P < 0.05$; ** $P < 0.01$; *** $P < 0.001$.   (↑), increase; (↓) decrease.
Degrees of freedom: $a = 4$; $b = 2$; $a+b = 8$; error = 14.

factorial experiment and Table 3 shows that this is primarily an effect of the sulphur dioxide in the presence of nitrogen dioxide, and that a synergistic interaction between the two gases enhances the effect of the sulphur dioxide. The same is also the case for peroxidase and GPT activities. RuDPC activity, however, is depressed by sulphur dioxide and there is no synergistic interaction, whilst GS activity is not significantly affected by any of the treatments!

Effects of sulphur dioxide plus ammonia on pea seedlings

Surveys on the Heysham peninsula have also shown high levels of ammonia, in the range 0.1–1 ppm, in addition to sulphur dioxide and nitrogen dioxide. A preliminary investigation of possible sulphur dioxide and ammonia interactions on enzyme activities was carried out prior to a full three-component investigation. The results of this initial study are shown in Tables 4 and 5.

Table 4. *Changes in glutamate dehydrogenase (GDH) activity in 14-day-old pea seedlings fumigated for the final 6 days with different levels of SO_2 and NH_3*

NH_3 (ppm)	SO_2 (ppm)			
	0	0.1	0.3	0.5
0	100	104	110	137
0.1	101	103	112	146
0.25	103	105	137	173
0.5	113	118	167	215

Values expressed as % of unpolluted controls.

Table 5. *F values and significance levels from a 4 × 4 factorial experiment to test for SO_2, NH_3 and $SO_2 + NH_3$ effects on enzymic activities of pea seedlings*

Enzyme	SO_2[a]	NH_3[b]	SO_2[a]$+NH_3$[b]
Ribulose-1,5-diphosphate carboxylase (RuDPC)	1.80	2.20	0.70
Peroxidase	8.40***(↑)	2.69*(↑)	1.40
Glutamate pyruvate transaminase (GPT)	0.18	1.00	3.70*(↓)
Glutamate dehydrogenase (GDH)	61.60***(↑)	24.61***(↑)	3.87**(↑)
Glutamine synthetase (GS)	0.24	2.10	0.53
Lipoxidase	1.66	1.52	1.26

[a] 0, 0.1, 0.3 and 0.5 ppm SO_2.

[b] 0, 0.1, 0.25 and 0.5 ppm NH_3.

* $P < 0.05$; ** $P < 0.01$; *** $P < 0.001$.   (↑), increase; (↓), decrease.
Degrees of freedom: $a = 3$; $b = 3$; $a+b = 9$; error $= 15$.

GDH activity was found to be stimulated even more by this mixture (Table 4) and a primary effect of the ammonia, in the presence of sulphur dioxide, was indicated by analysis of variance in addition to a sulphur dioxide effect and a synergistic interaction between the two gases (Table 5). The primary ammonia effect is probably due to the fact that the NH_4^+ ion is a substrate for GDH. Peroxidase also showed an ammonia effect but there was no synergistic interaction between sulphur dioxide and ammonia for this enzyme. Interestingly, an interaction between sulphur dioxide and ammonia was shown on the activity of GPT with the absence of individual primary effects.

Effects of nitric oxide, nitrogen dioxide plus propylene on tomato plants

Another polluted environment may be found in carbon-dioxide-enriched glasshouses where propane is burnt to produce carbon dioxide. In this process atmospheric nitrogen is converted to nitric oxide (NO) and this is oxidised at a very much slower rate to nitrogen dioxide in glasshouses than in the outside atmosphere because ozone levels are lower. The levels of these oxides of nitrogen can be quite high and may contribute to tissue damage (Capron & Mansfield, 1975). A survey of changes in enzyme activities has been carried out in parallel to a full physiological investigation using tomato

Table 6. *Changes in nitrite reductase activity in 6-week-old tomato seedlings fumigated for the final 3 weeks with different combinations of NO, NO_2 and C_3H_6*

Pollutant	None	C_3H_6* (50 ppm)
None	100	79
NO (0.4 ppm)	107	134
NO_2 (0.1 ppm)	102	95
$NO + NO_2$ (0.4+0.1 ppm)	107	107

Values expressed as % of unpolluted controls.

* Duration: 30 min every 24 h.

Table 7. *F values and significance levels from a $2 \times 2 \times 2$ factorial experiment to test for NO, NO_2, C_3H_6, $NO+NO_2$, $NO+C_3H_6$, $NO_2+C_3H_6$, and $NO+NO_2+C_3H_6$ effects on enzyme activities of tomato seedlings*

Enzyme	NO (0.4 ppm)	NO_2 (0.1 ppm)	C_3H_6† (50 ppm)	$NO+NO_2$	$NO+C_3H_6$	$NO_2+C_3H_6$	$NO+NO_2+C_3H_6$
Ribulose-1,5-diphosphate carboxylase (RuDPC)	0.04	0.03	0.04	0.00	0.68	0.08	0.06
Peroxidase	15.75**(↑)	0.32	1.22	0.63	0.36	0.27	3.67
Glutamate pyruvate transaminase (GPT)	2.02	0.18	0.01	0.28	1.17	1.14	0.05
Glutamate oxaloacetate transaminase (GOT)	2.86	3.08	1.12	0.92	0.74	0.86	2.32
Nitrite reductase	8.65*(↑)	0.12	0.00	2.76	4.11	0.29	2.19

* $P < 0.05$; ** $P < 0.01$.

† For 30 min every 24 h.

(↑), increase; (↓), decrease.

One degree of freedom for each treatment; 8 for error.

plants, one of the commonest glasshouse crops. In these studies the environmental situation has been modelled in fumigation cabinets. Traces of propylene (C_3H_6) are also found in glasshouses after the burners are turned on
and consequently this pollutant was also incorporated in the study. The
results for nitrite reductase are shown in Table 6 whilst the data from the
analysis of variance are shown in Table 7.

Nitrite reductase activity is shown to be significantly affected by nitric
oxide, as is the level of peroxidase activity. No other effect was detected but
it must be pointed out that for technical reasons the number of degrees of
freedom of the overall experiment was low and the sensitivity of the analysis
was much reduced as a consequence.

Fumigation experiments with Rumex seedlings from different origins

Evolution is a progressive phenomenon and is influenced by pollution, as
the papers in this volume by Bradshaw, Ernst and Bell & Mudd well illustrate.
There are no data at the biochemical level to demonstrate that cellular
adaptation has taken place in response to prolonged exposure to gaseous
atmospheric pollutants.

In preliminary experiments we have exposed *Rumex* seedlings of different
origins (amongst the highest and lowest in terms of average sulphur dioxide
levels for north-west England, as recorded by the Warren Springs Survey)
to both clean air and polluted air and determined any differences in enzyme
activity in the different 'strains' under different environmental conditions.
In Table 8 the enzyme activities of seedlings from Widnes, a very heavily
polluted industrial region of long standing, are compared to those in seedlings
originating from Thornton-Cleveleys, an area which is subjected to salt spray

Table 8. *Changes in peroxidase and ribulose-1,5-diphosphate
carboxylase (RuDPC) activities of 6-week-old plants of* Rumex
obtusifolius *from two different origins subjected to clean air or
polluted air (0.20 ppm SO_2) for 11 days*

Treatment	Peroxidase		Ribulose-1,5-diphosphate carboxylase	
	Thornton-Cleveleys	Widnes	Thornton-Cleveleys	Widnes
Clean air	100	160**	100	78*
Clean air + SO_2 (0.20 ppm)	128*	105	70**	122

Values expressed as % of *relevant* control.

* $P < 0.1$; ** $P < 0.05$.

and only small amounts of pollution from domestic sources. In the case of RuDPC activity the latter seedlings show inhibition in polluted air whilst those from the polluted environment are less 'efficient' in clean air but are more at home in the polluted situation. We have found this type of diagonal relationship with other enzyme activities. Levels of peroxidase activity are slightly different. Those plants originating from Widnes always have higher levels which remain unchanged, but those from an unpolluted area respond to the polluted situation by an increase in peroxidase activity.

Discussion

Throughout these studies we have been aware of a multitude of factors which may have an effect on enzyme activity. Some of them we have investigated and others warrant future attention. Nevertheless we have been at pains to maintain constancy in many parameters in order to evaluate a particular factor. Factors like light, temperature, humidity, water relations, nutrition, wind speed and tissue age have been taken into account. Endogenous rhythms no doubt take place but by sampling at the same time within the 24-h regime we trust that errors due to them have been minimised.

The existence of variation in response towards gaseous air pollutants within populations is illustrated by the preliminary experiments on *Rumex*. At least two ecological surveys using enzyme activities as indicators are in the literature (Godzik, 1967; Keller, 1974). If in both these cases the pollution investigated is of recent origin they are used in a valid manner. However it would clearly be unwise to extend this general survey approach to areas of long-standing pollution where selection has had time to take place.

The enzyme studies here show more dramatically than previous physiological studies just how important it is to consider mixed pollutant situations and the interactions that may be involved. Mixed situations are probably far commoner in urban and industrial environments than the wealth of single pollutant studies in the literature would imply. Future attention to interactions of various types will hopefully supply more information relevant to the situation in the field.

These studies, like nearly every other, have been carried out with steady levels of pollutants. Again this is far from the normal situation and in future we will concentrate on intermittent and fluctuating levels of different pollutants. There is a prevailing dogma that one should study steady and very low levels of pollutant. Any study that uses higher levels, however short-term, is likely to be stigmatised as unrealistic despite the fact that transients which undoubtedly occur in urban and industrial environments even exceed these levels. A departure from steady-level studies and simulations of the misleading 24-h mean will probably prove more realistic. Such studies may give an indication that fluctuating levels of a pollutant cause more stress than steady levels to which the plant can more easily adapt at the cellular and physiological level.

Throughout our enzyme studies we have not detected 'visible' injury of any kind. Chlorophyll levels may have changed a little but usually in the reverse direction, i.e. tissue treated with nitric oxide, nitrogen dioxide and ammonia often looked greener and contained more chlorophyll than corresponding control tissue. There is a temptation to ascribe the type of enzyme activity changes described here and elsewhere as justification for the existence of 'invisible' injury. This should be resisted because the cell is basically a self-regulating entity. Individual and synergistic biochemical changes are mitigated by additional and overlying mechanisms within the cell so that corresponding changes are often not shown at the physiological level. To counteract these cellular revolutions, energy and materials are required which would otherwise be available for growth and structural regeneration. Once energy and material expenditure on mitigation exceeds the input of energy and materials, 'visible injury' will inevitably follow. One should therefore view the effect of pollutants upon this dynamic and homeostatic system as a progressive energy and material displacement phenomenon and not argue about whether 'invisible injury' exists or not.

We are grateful to NERC and ARC for grants to assist us in this work and to Dr T. A. Mansfield and Dr R. Willix for helpful assistance and advice.

References

Bull, J. N. & Mansfield, T. A. (1974). Photosynthesis in leaves exposed to SO_2 and NO_2. *Nature, London* **250**, 443–4.

Capron, T. M. & Mansfield, T. A. (1975). Generation of nitrogen oxide pollutants during CO_2 enrichment of glasshouse atmospheres. *Journal of Horticultural Science* **50**, 233–8.

Godzik, S. (1967). Polyphenol oxidase activity in vegetation injured by industrial air pollution. *Biuletyn Zakladu Badań Nauk* **10**, 103–13.

Haydar, M. & Hadziyev, D. (1973). A study of lipoxidase in pea seeds and seedlings. *Journal of the Science of Food and Agriculture* **24**, 1039–53.

Horsman, D. C. & Wellburn, A. R. (1975). Synergistic effect of SO_2 and NO_2 polluted air upon enzyme activity in pea seedlings. *Environmental Pollution* **8**, 123–33.

Keller, Th. (1974). The use of peroxidase activity for monitoring and mapping air pollution areas. *European Journal of Forest Pathology* **4**, 11–19.

Majernik, O. & Mansfield, T. A. (1970). Direct effect of SO_2 pollution on the degree of opening of stomata. *Nature, London* **227**, 377–8.

Majernik, O. & Mansfield, T. A. (1971). Effects of SO_2 pollution on stomatal movements in *Vicia faba. Phytopathologische Zeitschrift* **71**, 123–8.

Mansfield, T. A. & Majernik, O. (1970). Can stomata play a part in protecting plants against air pollutants? *Environmental Pollution* **1**, 149–54.

Pahlich, E., Jäger, H-J. & Steubing, L. (1972). Beeinflussung der Aktivitäten von Glutamat dehydrogenase und Glutaminsynthetase aus Erbsenkeimlingen durch SO_2. *Angewandte Botanik* **46**, 183–97.

Pahlich, E. & Joy, K. W. (1971). Glutamate dehydrogenase from pea roots: purification and properties of the enzyme. *Canadian Journal of Biochemistry* **49**, 127–38.

Racker, E. (1963). *Modern methods of enzymatic analysis.* Academic Press, New York & London.

Weatherburn, M. W. (1967). Phenol hypochlorite reaction for determination of ammonia. *Analytical Chemistry* **39**, 971–4.

Wellburn, A. R., Majernik, O. & Wellburn, F. A. M. (1972). Effects of SO_2 and NO_2 polluted air upon the ultrastructure of chloroplasts. *Environmental Pollution* **3**, 37–49.

W.ERNST

Physiological and biochemical aspects of metal tolerance

Regional aerial pollution by heavy metals is as old as the smelting of these elements by man, as shown for lead by analysis of peat deposits in Great Britain (Lee & Tallis, 1973) and Germany (Ernst, Mathys, Salaske & Janiesch, 1974). But worldwide pollution of our environment with heavy metals as a result of human activities (see Murozumi, Chow & Patterson, 1969) has increased the attention being paid to the hazard of these elements as contaminants of soils, plants, animals and man. An important area of study arises from the fact that plants may accumulate heavy metals either from foliar deposits or by uptake through their roots. Aerial metal pollutants produced by metal smelters (Ernst, 1972a; Lee, 1972; Little & Martin, 1972; Buchauer, 1973; Wagner & Siddiqui, 1973; Hutchinson & Whitby, 1974), by combustion engines (Cannon & Bowles, 1962; Suchodoller, 1967; Lagerwerff, Armiger & Specht, 1973) or by high-tension lines (Hemkes & Hartmans, 1973; Ernst et al., 1974; Kraal & Ernst, 1975) can affect all plant organs. Although the literature abounds with reports related to various aspects of effects of heavy metals on plants, it is only recently that attention has been directed towards the physiological mechanisms possessed by those plants which are tolerant to these pollutants.

This paper attempts to elucidate the physiological and biochemical processes which give rise to heavy metal tolerance.

The evolution of heavy metal tolerance after aerial pollution

It is well-known that plant species from metalliferous soils have evolved specific tolerance to those heavy metals which are abundant in the soil (for recent reviews see Antonovics, Bradshaw & Turner, 1971; Ernst, 1974). However, this does not mean that tolerance to one metal confers tolerance to other metals; for example, plant species growing on copper-rich soils are only tolerant to copper, but not to zinc. There is evidence that aerial lead pollution from combustion engines has operated on plant populations to produce metal-tolerant individuals (Briggs, 1972, for *Marchantia polymorpha*). Industrial emission of zinc, cadmium, nickel and copper can also cause such processes of evolution (Table 1) (Bradshaw, McNeilly & Gregory, 1965; Wu & Bradshaw, 1972; Ernst, Mathys & Janiesch, 1975; Ernst, unpublished

Table 1.   *Mean index of copper and zinc tolerance of* Agrostis *populations in areas of atmospheric pollution with heavy metals*

Plant species and type of pollution	Duration (yr)	Heavy metal in soil (μg atom g^{-1})	Index of tolerance against: Copper	Zinc
Agrostis canina[a]				
Galvanised fence	22	Zinc: 2 (avail.)†	—	0.95*
Agrostis stolonifera[b]				
Copper refinery	8	Copper: 75	0.30	—
	70	Copper: 67	0.60*	—
Agrostis tenuis[c]				
Zinc and cadmium	5	Zinc: 185		1.17**
refinery		Copper: 3	0.14	

[a] Bradshaw *et al.* (1965); [b] Wu & Bradshaw (1972); [c] Ernst *et al.* (1975).

* Significant difference from populations in non-contaminated areas.

† Available zinc, i.e. extractable zinc concentration in the soil.

data for *Agrostis tenuis*). But most plants present initially in areas polluted with heavy metals are not sufficiently resistant, so that they are damaged by the metal pollutants. Their leaves become chlorotic or necrotic and contain large amounts of the aerial pollutant. Long-lived plants, such as shrubs and

Table 2.   *Concentration of heavy metals in leaves of plants in areas surrounding smelting operations*

Plant species	Metal	Metal content (μg atom g^{-1} dry matter)	Reference
Aesculus hippocastanum	Zinc	242.0	Ernst *et al.* (1974)
Fragaria vesca	Copper	33.1	Ernst (unpublished data)
Grasses	Lead	32.4*	Vetter & Mählhop (1971)
Deschampsia flexuosa	Nickel	15.3	Hutchinson & Whitby (1974)
	Copper	11.4	
Thlaspi alpestre	Cadmium	10.0	Denaeyer-De Smet (1974)

* Not washed.

trees, are unable to evolve metal-tolerant ecotypes, whereas grasses and some dicotyledons are successful colonisers of these areas, despite the high metal concentration in their leaves (Table 2). The ability to evolve metal tolerance is species-specific (Gartside & McNeilly, 1974) and independent of the source of contamination.

The mechanisms of heavy metal tolerance

The mechanisms whereby plants can combat toxic levels of heavy metals are as follows:

(1) *avoidance*, as defined by Levitt (1958), i.e. an exclusion mechanism by prevention of metal uptake;

(2) *tolerance*, also as defined by Levitt (1958), where uptake occurs but resistance is due to exclusion of metals from metal-sensitive sites, formation of specific metal-resistant enzymes or alteration of metabolic pathways.

Heavy-metal resistance by avoidance

This form of heavy metal resistance ought to be the best. However, in all experiments with metal tolerant and non-tolerant populations of *Agrostis tenuis* (Bradshaw *et al.*, 1965; Mathys, 1973), *Silene cucubalus* (Ernst, 1972a), *Anthoxanthum odoratum* (M. H. Sindrey & J. C. Collins, personal communication), *Armeria maritima* and *Thlaspi alpestre* (Ernst, unpublished data) it could be demonstrated that no mechanism exists which can prevent heavy metals entering resistant plants. Nevertheless, external conditions can influence the uptake pattern for different metals. Thus, organic compounds containing heavy metals are taken up by plants more slowly than ionic metals (Turner & Gregory, 1967; Ernst, 1968a; Schiller, 1974). The absorption rate of heavy metals can be reduced in the presence of higher amounts of calcium (Jowett, 1964) and phosphorus (Ernst, 1968a) or by competition for the same carrier (Bowen, 1969; Ernst, 1972a; Mathys, 1973; Ernst *et al.*, 1974). But generally, even heavy metal tolerant plants cannot prevent the uptake of these ions. Therefore, all the plants growing on metalliferous areas are rich in heavy metals (Table 3). Despite the general consistency of patterns of uptake of copper, zinc, lead, nickel and cadmium, populations of the same species may differ in metal content. Ernst (1972a) provided evidence that a low cation exchange capacity of the roots significantly reduced the absorption rate of zinc and copper (Table 4); however, the selection for cation exchange capacity is genetically independent of heavy metal tolerance. There exists no exclusion mechanism.

Table 3. *Highest values of heavy metals in leaves and roots of plants without symptoms of metal toxicity*

Plant species	Metal	Metal content (μg atom g^{-1} dry matter)	Organ	Reference
Psychotria douarrei	Nickel	772 1580	Leaf Root	Jaffré & Schmid (1974)
Thlaspi alpestre	Zinc	382 173	Leaf Root	Ernst (1975)
Minuartia verna	Lead	55 127	Leaf Root	Ernst (1974)
Trachypogon spicatus	Copper	0.1 43	Leaf Root	Reilly & Reilly (1973)
Pearsonia metallifera	Chromium	9 31	Leaf Root	Ernst (1975)
Acrocephalus robertii	Cobalt	25	Leaf	Duvigneaud & Denaeyer-De Smet (1960)
Minuartia verna	Cadmium	3.1 3.4	Leaf Root	Ernst (1975)
Cynodon plectostachyum	Arsenic	0.3 0.3	Leaf Root	Wild (1974 and unpublished data)

Table 4. *Zinc and copper uptake of zinc-tolerant, copper-tolerant and non-tolerant populations of* Silene cucubalus *grown for 4 weeks in a full nutrient solution with 0.05 mM zinc and 0.05 mM copper, in relation to cation exchange capacity (CEC) of the roots*

	Non-tolerant Brochterbeck	Zinc-tolerant Blankenrode	Copper-tolerant Marsberg	Copper-tolerant Imsbach
Uptake of zinc (μg atom per g dry matter of roots)	101.0	107.0	93.1	50.0*
Uptake of copper (μg atom per g dry matter of roots)	77.6	78.5	75.5	31.6*
CEC of roots (m-equiv. per 100 g dry matter)	31.7	29.1	28.5	20.3*

After Ernst (1972a).

* Highly significant at $P = 0.05$.

Heavy-metal resistance by tolerance mechanisms

Heavy metal resistance seems to imply a special internal metabolism. Although some of the heavy metals have essential functions in metabolism, any surplus of these elements may cause toxicity in non-tolerant plants. Metal-tolerant plants have to resist this toxic effect by removing these ions from the metabolism, by rendering them into an innocuous form or by changing enzyme structures.

Importance of the cell wall   The exclusion of heavy metals from susceptible sites in the protoplasm is normally an avoidance at the cellular level. Despite the marked chemical differences in cell walls within the plant kingdom, a high affinity of heavy metals for cell membranes is found in bacteria (Tornabene & Edwards, 1972; Uchida, Saito, Kaziwara & Enomoto, 1973), in fungi (Somers, 1963; Ashida, Higashi & Kikuchi, 1963; Venkateswerlu & Silvarama Sastry, 1970), and for cell walls in algae and in angiosperms (Cartwright, 1966; Peterson, 1969; Turner, 1970; Reilly, Rowel & Stone, 1970). Especially important is the fact that more than 90% of the chromium and lead is usually bound to cell walls in roots and shoots (Ernst, 1972b) and therefore only very low amounts of these elements reach the plasma of the cells. This is one of the reasons why no severe problems arise for the metabolism of plants when they are contaminated with lead from automobile exhausts (Steenken, 1973) as the benzine lead is only accumulated on the plant and in the cuticula of the leaves and shoots. However, for herbivorous animals the benzine lead remains a serious problem because it is accumulated up the food chain (Welch & Dick, 1975; Mierau & Favara, 1975).

   Independent of this general behaviour of heavy metals in cell walls, Peterson (1969), Turner (1970) and Mathys (1973) presented evidence that roots of zinc-tolerant populations of *Agrostis tenuis* contained appreciably more zinc in the cell wall fraction than did the corresponding fraction of non-tolerant populations (Table 5). A further indication that the binding capacity for zinc in the cell wall may be part of the zinc tolerance mechanism seems to come from the work of Turner & Marshall (1972). They found a significant correlation between accumulation by the cell wall fraction and the index of zinc tolerance of the populations ($y = 0.004 x$) of *Agrostis tenuis* originating in the British Isles. However, zinc-tolerant populations of the same species from Germany do not fit into this scheme ($y = 0.56$). In addition, at high levels of zinc nutrition, different zinc-tolerant populations inactivate quite different amounts of zinc ions in the root cell walls. Therefore, this phenomenon may help to explain just one feature of metal tolerance, and it may be related to metabolic events in the cytoplasm (Malone, Koeppe

Table 5. *Per cent distribution of zinc in the roots of populations*
of Agrostis tenuis *grown at different zinc levels*

Population	Zinc content in the nutrient solution (μM)	% of total zinc in cell wall	Reference
Non-tolerant			
New Zealand	0.8	24.3	Peterson (1969)
	75	33.6	
Weiberg	1	44.2	Mathys (1973)
	200	34.0	
Copper-tolerant			
Parys Mountain	1	39.5	Turner (1970)
	115	56.2	
Marsberg	1	41.5	Mathys (1973)
	200	33·0	
Zinc-tolerant			
Goginan	0.8	80.7	Peterson (1969)
	75	67.3	
Trelogan	1	60.7	Turner (1970)
	115	90.6	
Blankenrode	1	41.9	Mathys (1973)
	50	47.4	
	200	51.6	

& Miller, 1974). Other mechanisms must be involved in shoots and leaves, where the preferential localisation of zinc and copper may occur in the vacuoles. To reach the vacuoles, large amounts of heavy metals have to pass through the protoplasm and there they may interact with metal-sensitive structures (Ernst, 1968b, 1974; Kjuregjan & Burnutjan, 1973).

The importance of the protoplasm   The precise mechanism of a specific heavy metal tolerance in the cytoplasm has to be sought in the part of the cell between the plasmalemma and the tonoplast. Three kinds of mechanism are possible:
(1) an intensive carrier, transporting heavy metals from the cell wall through to the vacuole;
(2) the evolution of specific metal-resistant enzymes;
(3) alteration in the cell's metabolism.
In experiments with *Agrostis tenuis* and *Silene cucubalus* it was not possible to detect any increased transport of heavy metals by carriers, perhaps in accordance with a passive uptake mechanism for zinc (Findenegg & Broda,

1965; Joseph, Rathore, Bajaj & Wittwer, 1971), cobalt (Craig Colclasure & Schmid, 1974) and cadmium (Cutler & Rains, 1974). Therefore, the idea of especially active or more numerous carriers in metal-tolerant plants has no experimental support.

The possibility of the evolution of special enzymes resistant to heavy metals is realised in *Mycobacterium tuberculosis avium* (Horio, Higashi & Okunuki, 1956) and in *Saccharomyces cerevisiae* (Murayama, 1961). In both organisms, several stages of the tricarboxylic acid cycle are not inhibited by copper in tolerant strains, in contrast to the situation in non-tolerant populations. However, no indication of the evolution of especially metal-resistant enzymes has been found in metal-tolerant angiosperms. Mathys (1975) and Ernst (unpublished data) demonstrated that, *in vitro*, nitrate reductase (NR), isocitrate dehydrogenase (ICDH), glucose-6-phosphate dehydrogenase (G6P-DH), malate dehydrogenase (MDH), peroxidase (PO) and acid phosphatase obtained from copper-, lead-, and zinc-tolerant populations of *Silene cucubalus* and *Silene nutans* are as sensitive to copper, zinc, lead, nickel, cobalt, cadmium and manganese as the same enzymes from non-tolerant populations of these species (Table 6). However, the different heavy metals affect the enzymes in different ways, depending on their affinity for sulphydryl (Miller, Bittel & Koeppe, 1973) and carboxylic groups (Vallee & Ulmer,

Table 6. *Concentrations of heavy metals (mM) inhibiting 50% of activity of nitrate reductase (NR), malate dehydrogenase (MDH), isocitrate dehydrogenase (ICDH), glucose-6-phosphate dehydrogenase (G6P-DH) and peroxidase (PO) of leaves of different metal tolerant populations of* Silene cucubalus

Treatment	NR	MDH	ICDH	G6P-DH	PO
Zinc					
Zinc-tolerant	0.006	1.40	0.17	0.36	5.12
Copper-tolerant	0.006	1.46	0.16	0.35	5.07
Zinc/copper-tolerant	0.007	1.43	0.16	0.34	5.09
Non-tolerant	0.006	1.46	0.17	0.35	5.14
Copper					
Zinc-tolerant	0.0007	0.38	0.40	0.001	0.12
Copper-tolerant	0.0007	0.39	0.40	0.001	0.12
Zinc/copper-tolerant	0.0006	0.38	0.42	0.001	0.13
Non-tolerant	0.0007	0.38	0.42	0.001	0.12

After Mathys (1975) and Ernst (unpublished data).

122   W. ERNST

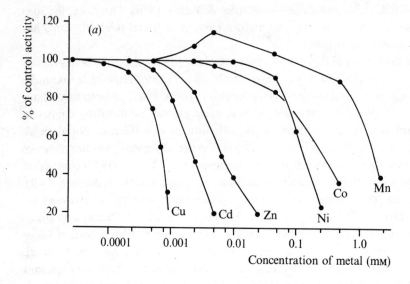

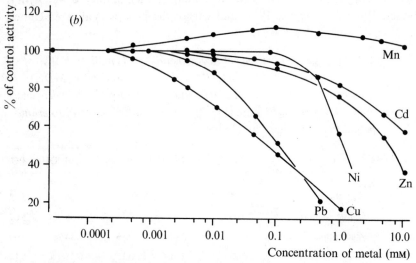

Fig. 1.   The effects of some heavy metals (except lead all as sulphate)
added to the incubation medium on the activity of (*a*) nitrate reductase
(NR; after Mathys, 1975) and (*b*) peroxidase (PO; Ernst, unpublished data)
of leaves from a zinc-resistant population of *Silene cucubalus*. Activity of
NR control (100%) = 2.8 μM NO$_2$ g^{-1} h^{-1}; activity of PO control
(100%) = 72 000 ΔOD at 420 nm g^{-1} min^{-1}, using guaiacol as substrate.

1972). Therefore, sulphydryl-containing enzymes like, for example, NR, are very sensitive to heavy metals (Fig. 1a), whereas peroxidases (Fig. 1b) and MDH are relatively resistant in all populations. Compared with the cytoplasmic heavy metal resistance of copper-tolerant populations of *Silene cucubalus* (Gries, 1966; Ernst, 1972a, 1974) and *Silene nutans*, the in-vitro resistance of MDH, ICDH and PO is sufficient to confer tolerance to high amounts of copper in the cell, but not, however, to a high zinc content.

This outline of our present studies can be compared with the known behaviour of enzymes in plants growing in other habitats with high mineral levels. Enzymes of angiospermous halophytes are as sensitive to sodium chloride as those of salt-intolerant species (Flowers, 1972; Greenway & Osmond, 1972; Greenway & Sims, 1974; Osmond & Greenway, 1972; Austenfeld, 1974); however, the physiological basis of heavy metal and salt tolerance may be completely different. Fluoride-tolerant plants of Africa also contain no specific fluoride-resistant enzymes (Eloff & Sydow, 1971). It appears that the evolution of heavy-metal-resistant (Horio *et al.*, 1955; Murayama, 1961) and salt-resistant enzymes (Holmes & Halvorson, 1963; Liebl, Kaplan & Kushner, 1969) is restricted to micro-organisms. Therefore, we must presume that the high specificity of metal tolerance in angiosperms is dependent on cells as they already exist, and not to a fundamental change in their constituents.

The behaviour of enzymes of angiosperms *in vivo* is quite different compared with that in experiments *in vitro*. This difference in behaviour was found in different metal-resistant populations of *Silene cucubalus* and *Silene nutans* (Ernst *et al.*, 1975; Mathys, 1975). A concentration of 0.4 mM Zn in nutrient solution drastically reduced the nitrate reductase activity of populations of *Silene cucubalus* not tolerant to zinc, whereas in the zinc-tolerant population this enzyme not only functioned normally, but was essentially stimulated in the presence of larger amounts of zinc (Table 7). The consequence of a reduced activity of the NR at high zinc levels is an increase in the nitrate level of the leaves of these non-tolerant populations (Ernst *et al.*, 1975). In contrast, the stimulation of NR in tolerant populations suggests that the enzyme requires more zinc for optimal functioning of physiological processes, especially for protein synthesis. This is in accordance with the fact that metal-resistant populations of different species show optimum biomass production at higher metal levels (Baumeister, 1954; Ernst, 1972a; Dikanskaya, 1971; Cook, Lefébvre & McNeilly, 1972; Schiller, 1974).

Smaller effects of zinc were observed for other enzymes. ICDH is stimulated or retarded in the same manner as NR. In contrast to these two enzymes, the activity of G6P-DH is diminished by zinc in the tolerant population and stimulated in the non-tolerant ones. The high activity of the G6P-DH of zinc-tolerant plants at low zinc concentrations can also be interpreted as a deficiency symptom, as a similar response has been shown in potassium-deficient plants (Kinzel & Stummerer, 1974). The activity of MDH remained nearly unchanged in all populations after the addition of zinc, comparable with the reaction of this enzyme during ammonium and salt stress (Wakiuchi, Matsumoto & Takahashi, 1971; Willert, 1974; Greenway & Sims, 1974).

Table 7. *In-vivo activity of some enzymes* (μM *substrate* h^{-1} *per g fresh wt*) *of leaves from* Silene cucubalus *populations cultivated 4 weeks with and without zinc in the nutrient solution*

| | Population | | | | | |
| | Zinc-tolerant | | Non-tolerant | | Copper-tolerant | |
Enzyme	Control	0.4 mM Zn	Control	0.4 mM Zn	Control	0.4 mM Zn
NR	3.2	5.5	6.3	0.9	5.2	1.2
ICDH	15.7	19.9	12.3	10.2	18.1	16.9
G6P-DH	22.6	12.4	10.3	14.2	19.3	25.8
MDH	2890.0	2760.0	3150.0	2780.0	2770.0	2830.0

After Mathys (1975).

Nevertheless, the addition of zinc influenced the number of MDH isoenzymes in zinc-tolerant and non-tolerant populations in zymograms, identified by means of gel electrophoresis (Ernst *et al.*, 1975; Fig. 2). Therefore, we have to be very careful in the interpretation of the activity of isoenzymes. Woolhouse (1970) using a different approach, namely measurement of the acid phosphatase activity of intact root tips, noted a greater loss of activity in lead-intolerant plants compared with tolerant *Agrostis tenuis*. The foregoing evidence of differential metal activation and inhibition of enzymes in different metal-tolerant populations must imply that particular metabolites protect metal-sensitive structures and thus provide a means of coping with excess metal ions.

Alterations in the nature of metabolites are known to occur. Studies of heavy metal tolerance of micro-organisms have revealed that in some of them tolerance is due to a pool of sulphydryl groups. The increase of these groups or stimulation of metallomethionine synthesis is widespread in animals after heavy metal contamination (e.g. Ono *et al.*, 1973; Shank & Vetter, 1974), although these events are not correlated with metal resistance. In the plant kingdom, increases in non-protein sulphydryl groups are known to accompany mercury tolerance in *Aspergillus niger* (Ashworth & Amin, 1964) and copper tolerance in *Saccharomyces cerevisiae* (Ashida & Nakamura, 1959),

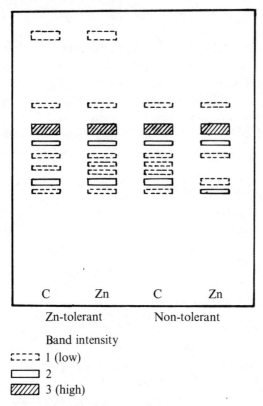

Fig. 2. Diagrammatic representation of malate dehydrogenase (MDH) isoenzymes in leaves of the same age from zinc-tolerant and non-tolerant *Silene cucubalus* grown in a medium without (C) and with zinc (Zn; 0.4 mM). (After Ernst *et al.*, 1975.)

whereas a decrease in sulphydryl groups characterises the metabolism of non-tolerant plants (Cedeno-Maldonado & Swader, 1974). However, Seno (1963) found no genetic correlation between metal tolerance and the production of sulphydryl groups in yeasts. Similar studies of metal-tolerant angiosperms did not give any indication of an overactive sulphur metabolism, with the exception of mustard oils in resistant Crucifereae (Mathys, 1975 and personal communication).

The formation of stable metalloproteins has been discussed for copper- and cadmium-resistant bacteria (Uchida *et al.*, 1973; Tokuyama & Asano, 1974). Also Reilly (1972) mentioned the possibility of copper-chelation by peptide in copper-tolerant populations of *Becium homblei*. On the basis of the high degree of specificity of heavy metal tolerance, Woolhouse (1970) supports this idea. But Turner (1969), Peterson (1969), Reilly & Reilly (1973) and

Ernst *et al.* (1975) did not find such special metalloproteins in zinc- and copper-tolerant plants.

Analysing the organic acids of the tricarboxylic acid cycle, we (Ernst *et al.*, 1975) found marked differences between zinc-tolerant and zinc-intolerant populations of diverse angiosperms. Zinc-tolerant plants of *Silene cucubalus*, *Thlaspi alpestre* and *Agrostis tenuis* have essentially higher amounts of malic acid than zinc-intolerant ones. This is also true for populations which recently have evolved zinc tolerance within 5 years after heavy aerial zinc pollution (Table 8). In addition, zinc-tolerant populations of *Silene*

Table 8.   *Malic acid content in the leaves of non-tolerant, copper-tolerant, and zinc-tolerant populations of some plant species*

Species (population)	Malic acid (μM g^{-1} fresh wt)
Agrostis tenuis	
Non-tolerant	0.89 ± 0.13
Copper-tolerant	1.07 ± 0.02
Zinc-tolerant	1.65 ± 0.11
Zinc-tolerant (air pollution)	1.72 ± 0.15
Silene cucubalus	
Non-tolerant	2.18 ± 0.32
Copper-tolerant	1.60 ± 0.33
Zinc-tolerant	9.78 ± 0.48
Thlaspi alpestre	
Non-tolerant	1.90 ± 0.05
Zinc-tolerant	12.84 ± 0.14

After Ernst *et al.* (1975).

cucubalus kept malic acid content at the same level after zinc treatment, in contrast to the decreasing content of zinc-intolerant plants, perhaps due to the diminished activity of ICDH and the accumulation of nitrate under zinc stress. A possible function of malic acid as a protecting agent, as known for some halophytes (Greenway & Sims, 1974) could not be detected in the enzymes of *Silene cucubalus* which were tested (Fig. 3). Perhaps other well-documented zinc complexes in plants (Bowen, Cawse & Thick, 1962; Gomah & Davies, 1974) may be more effective. The predominant function of malate in zinc-tolerant plants will be a zinc transfer from the plasma to the vacuole system. However, the specificity of zinc tolerance cannot be explained by the high level of malic acid alone, because copper can form complexes with malic acid with higher stability constants than those of zinc (Sillen & Martell, 1964). Therefore a further mechanism in the plasmalemma is necessary.

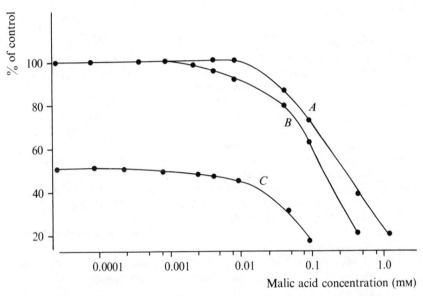

Fig. 3.   Effect of malic acid on the activity of peroxidase of leaves from zinc-tolerant *Silene cucubalus* in the absence of copper or zinc (*A*) and in the presence of 0.5 mM zinc sulphate (*B*) or 0.5 mM copper sulphate (*C*).

In contrast to the zinc-tolerant populations, copper tolerance seems to be regulated by complexing the copper in phenolic compounds, as already known from studies with *Rumex tianschanicus* under manganese stress (Pershukova & Levanidov, 1973) and *Saccharomyces* under cobalt stress (Dikanskaya, 1971). The formation of copper oxalates comparable to the trioxalatochromate complexes of chromium-resistant plants of *Leptospermum scoparium* (Lyon, Peterson & Brooks, 1969*a* and *b*) was not detected in the oxalate-producing populations of *Silene cucubalus*.

Although the actual sites of heavy metal action cannot be specified at this time, the data do suggest that the maintenance of metal tolerance requires much energy. Therefore tolerant plants normally have a lower biomass production (20–50% lower) and are not able to withstand competition with non-tolerant populations on normal soils. Perhaps the high specificity of metal tolerance is due to changes in a large number of physiological parameters which involve a lot of cellular activity.

I am greatly indebted to the Landesamt für Forschung des Landes Nordrhein-Westfalen, German Federal Republic, for partial financial support.

References

Antonovics, J., Bradshaw, A. D. & Turner, R. G. (1971). Heavy metal tolerance in plants. In *Advances in ecological research*, Ed. J. B. Cragg, vol. 7, pp. 1–85. Academic Press, New York & London.

Ashida, J., Higashi, N. & Kikuchi, T. (1963). An electronmicroscopic study on copper precipitation by copper-resistant yeast cells. *Protoplasma* 57, 27–32.

Ashida, J. & Nakamura, H. (1959). Role of sulfur metabolism in copper resistance of yeasts. *Plant and Cell Physiology* 1, 71–9.

Ashworth, L. J. & Amin, J. V. (1964). A mechanism for mercury tolerance in fungi. *Phytopathology* 54, 1459–63.

Austenfeld, F. A. (1974). Der Einfluss des NaCl und anderer Alkalisalze auf die Nitratreduktaseaktivität von *Salicornia europaea* L. *Zeitschrift für Pflanzenphysiologie* 71, 288–96.

Baumeister, W. (1954). Über den Einfluss des Zinks bei *Silene inflata* Sm. *Berichte der Deutschen Botanischen Gesellschaft* 67, 205–13.

Bowen, H. J. M., Cawse, P. A. & Thick, J. (1962). The distribution of some inorganic elements in plant tissue extracts *Journal of Experimental Botany* 13, 257–67.

Bowen, J. E. (1969). Absorption of copper, zinc and manganese by sugar-cane leaf tissue. *Plant Physiology* 44, 255–61.

Bradshaw, A. D., McNeilly, T. S. & Gregory, R. P. G. (1965). Industrialization, evolution and the development of heavy metal tolerance in plants. In *Ecology and the industrial society. British ecological society symposium*, Ed. G. T. Goodman *et al.* 5, pp. 327–43. Blackwell Scientific Publications, Oxford.

Briggs, D. (1972). Population differentiation in *Marchantia polymorpha* L. in various lead pollution levels. *Nature, London* 238, 166–7.

Buchauer, M. J. (1973). Contamination of soil and vegetation near a zinc smelter by zinc, cadmium, copper and lead. *Environmental Science and Technology* 7, 131–5.

Cannon, H. L. & Bowles, J. M. (1962). Contamination of vegetation by tetraethyl lead. *Science* 137, 765–6.

Cartwright, B. (1966). Studies on copper deficiency in nodulated subterranean clover. PhD thesis, University of Nottingham.

Cedeno-Maldonado, A. & Swader, J. A. (1974). Studies on the mechanism of copper toxicity in *Chlorella*. *Weed Science* 22, 443–9.

Cook, S. C. A., Lefébvre, C. & McNeilly, T. (1972). Competition between metal-tolerant and normal populations on normal soil. *Evolution* 26, 366–72.

Craig Colclasure, G. & Schmid, W. E. (1974). Absorption of cobalt by excised barley roots. *Plant and Cell Physiology* **15**, 273–9.

Crawford, R. M. M. (1966). The control of anaerobic respiration as a determining factor in the distribution of the genus *Senecio*. *Journal of Ecology* **54**, 403–13.

Cutler, J. M. & Rains, D. W. (1974). Characterization of cadmium uptake by plant tissue. *Plant Physiology* **54**, 67–71.

Denaeyer-De Smet, S. (1974). Premier aperçu de la distribution du cadmium dans divers écosystèmes terrestres non pollués et pollués. *Oecologia Plantarum* **9**, 169–82.

Dikanskaya, E. M. (1971). Yeast variants, producing riboflavin and resistant to cobalt. *Mikrobiologiya* **40**, 1077–83.

Duvigneaud, P. & Denaeyer-De Smet, S. (1960). Action de certains metaux lourds du sol (cuivre, cobalt, manganese, uranium) sur la végétation dans le Haut Katanga. In *Rapports de sol et de la végétation*, pp. 121–39. Masson, Paris.

Eloff, J. N. & Sydow, B. von (1971). Experiments on the fluoroacetate metabolism of *Dichapetalum cymosum* (Gifblaar). *Phytochemistry* **10**, 1409–15.

Ernst, W. (1968a). Der Einfluss der Phosphatversorgung sowie die Wirkung von ionogenem und chelatisiertem Zink auf die Zink- und Phosphataufnahme einiger Schwermetallpflanzen. *Physiologia Plantarum* **21**, 323–33.

Ernst, W. (1968b). Zur Kenntnis der Soziologie und Okologie der Schwermetall-vegetation Grossbritanniens. *Berichte der Deutschen Botanischen Gesellschaft* **81**, 116–24.

Ernst, W. (1972a). Schwermetallresistenz und Mineralstoffhaushalt. *Forschungsberichte des Landes Nordrhein-Westfalen* **2251**, 1–38.

Ernst, W. (1972b). Ecophysiological studies on heavy metal plants in South Central Africa. *Kirkia* **8**, 125–45.

Ernst, W. (1974). *Schwermetallvegetation der Erde.* G. Fischer Verlag, Stuttgart. 196 pp.

Ernst, W. (1975). Mechanismen der Schwermetallresistenz. In *Verhandlungen der Gesellschaft für Okologie, Erlangen 1974*, ed. by P. Müller, pp. 187–95.

Ernst, W., Mathys, W. & Janiesch, P. (1975). Physiologische Grundlagen der Schwermetallresistenz-Enzymaktivitäten und organische Säuren. *Forschungsberichte des Landes Nordrhein-Westfalen* **2496**, 1–50. Westdeutscher Verlag, Opladen.

Ernst, W., Mathys, W., Salaske, J. & Janiesch, P. (1974). Aspekte von Schwermetall-belastungen in Westfalen. *Abhandlungen Landesmuseum für Naturkunde zu Münster in Westfalen* **36** (2), 1–30.

Findenegg, G. & Broda, E. (1965). Mechanism of uptake of trace elements by plant roots. *Nature, London* **208**, 196–7.

Flowers, T. J. (1972). The effect of sodium chloride on enzyme activities from four halophyte species of Chenopodiaceae. *Phytochemistry* **11**, 1881–6.

Gartside, D. W. & McNeilly, T. (1974). The potential for evolution of heavy metal tolerance in plants. II. Copper tolerance in normal populations of different plant species. *Heredity* **32**, 335–48.

Gomah, A. M. & Davies, R. I. (1974). Identification of the active ligands chelating Zn in some plant water extracts. *Plant and Soil* **40**, 1–19.

Greenway, H. & Osmond, C. B. (1972). Salt responses of enzymes from species differing in salt tolerance. *Plant Physiology* **49**, 256–9.

Greenway, H. & Sims, A. P. (1974). Effects of high concentrations of KCl and NaCl on responses of malate dehydrogenase (decarboxylating) to malate and various inhibitors. *Australian Journal of Plant Physiology* 1, 15–29.

Gries, B. (1966). Zellphysiologische Untersuchungen über die Zinkresistenz bei Galmeiformen und Normalformen von *Silene cucubalus* Wib. *Flora, Jena* 156B, 271–90.

Hemkes, O. J. & Hartmans, J. (1973). Copper content in grass and soil under copper high-tension lines. *Tijdschrift voor Diergeneeskunde* 98, 446–9.

Holmes, P. K. & Halvorson, H. O. (1963). The inactivation and reactivation of salt requiring enzymes from an extreme obligate halophile. *Canadian Journal of Microbiology* 9, 904–6.

Horio, T., Higashi, T. & Okunuki, K. (1955). Copper resistance of *Mycobacterium tuberculosis* avium. II. The influence of copper ion on the respiration of the parent cells and copper-resistant cells. *Journal of Biochemistry, Tokyo* 42, 491–8.

Hutchinson, T. C. & Whitby, L. M. (1974). A study of airborne contamination of vegetation and soils by heavy metals from the Sudbury, Ontario, copper–nickel smelters. In *Trace substances in environmental health VII*, Ed. D. D. Hemphill, pp. 175–8. University of Missouri, Columbia.

Jaffré, T. & Schmid, M. (1974). Accumulation du nickel par une Rubiacée de Nouvelle-Calédonie, *Psychotria douarrei* (G. Beauvisage) Däniker. *Comptes rendus de l'Académie des Sciences, Paris*, Ser. D, 278, 1727–30.

Jowett, D. (1964). Population studies on lead-tolerant *Agrostis tenuis*. *Evolution* 18, 70–80.

Joseph, C., Rathore, V. S., Bajaj, Y. P. S. & Wittwer, S. H. (1971). Mechanism of zinc absorption by intact bean plants. *Annals of Botany* 35, 683–6.

Kinzel, H. & Stummerer, H. (1974). Enzymaktivitäts-Muster als Indikatoren für den physiologische Zustand von Pflanzen unter Mineralstoffmangel. *Berichte der Deutschen Botanischen Gesellschaft* 86, 505–12.

Kjuregjan, E. A. & Burnutjan, R. A. (1973). Copper, zinc and lead in plant sap. *Doklady Akademii nauk SSSR* 57, 103–7.

Kraal, H. & Ernst, W. (1975). Influence of copper high-tension lines on plants and soils. *Environmental Pollution*, in press.

Lagerwerff, J. V., Armiger, W. H. & Specht, A. W. (1973). Uptake of lead by alfalfa and corn from soil and air. *Soil Science* 115, 455–60.

Lee, J. A. (1972). Lead pollution from a factory manufacturing antiknock compounds. *Nature, London* 238, 165–6.

Lee, J. A. & Tallis, J. H. (1973). Regional and historical aspects of lead pollution in Britain. *Nature, London* 245, 216–18.

Levitt, J. (1958). Frost, drought and heat resistance. In *Protoplasmatologia, Handbuch der Protoplasmaforschung*, Eds L. V. Heilbrunn & F. Weber, vol. VII, p. 6. Springer-Verlag, Berlin.

Liebl, V., Kaplan, J. G. & Kushner, D. J. (1969). Regulation of a salt-dependent enzyme: the aspartate transcarbamylase of an extreme halophile. *Canadian Journal of Biochemistry* 47, 1095–7.

Little, P. & Martin, M. H. (1972). A survey of zinc, lead and cadmium in soil and natural vegetation around a smelting complex. *Environmental Pollution* 3, 241–54.

Lyon, G. L., Peterson, P. J. & Brooks, R. R. (1969a). Chromium-51 transport in the xylem sap of *Leptospermum scoparium* (Manuka). *New Zealand Journal of Science* **12**, 541–5.

Lyon, G. L., Peterson, P. J. & Brooks, R. R. (1969*b*). Chromium-51 distribution in tissues and extracts of *Leptospermum scoparium*. *Planta, Berlin* **88**, 282–7.

Malone, C., Koeppe, D. E. & Miller, R. J. (1974). Localisation of lead accumulated by corn plants. *Plant Physiology* **53**, 388–94.

Mathys, W. (1973). Vergleichende Untersuchungen der Zinkaufnahme von resistenten und sensitiven Populationen von *Agrostis tenuis* Sibth. *Flora, Jena* **162**, 492–9.

Mathys, W. (1975). Enzymes of heavy-metal-resistant and non-resistant populations of *Silene cucubalus* and their interaction with some heavy metals *in vitro* and *in vivo*. *Physiologia Plantarum* **33**, 161–5.

Mierau, G. W. & Favara, B. E. (1975). Lead poisoning in roadside populations of deer mice. *Environmental Pollution* **8**, 55–64.

Miller, R. J., Bittell, J. E. & Koeppe, D. E. (1973). The effect of cadmium on electron and energy transfer reactions in corn mitochondria. *Physiologia Plantarum* **28**, 166–71.

Murayama, T. (1961). Studies on the metabolic pattern of yeast with reference to its copper resistance. *Memoirs of the Ehime University*, Sect. II, Ser. B **4**, 43–66.

Murozumi, M., Chow, T. J. & Patterson, C. C. (1969). Chemical concentration of pollutant lead aerosols, terrestrial dust and sea salts in Greenland and Antarctic snow strata. *Geochimica et Cosmochimica Acta* **33**, 1247–94.

Ono, T., Wada, O., Nagahashi, M., Yamaguchi, N. & Tokokawa, K. (1973). Increase of sulfhydryl group in proteins from kidney of mice administered various heavy metals. *Indian Health* **11**, 73–4.

Osmond, C. B. & Greenway, H. (1972). Salt responses of carboxylating enzymes from species differing in salt tolerance. *Plant Physiology* **49**, 117–23.

Pershukova, A. M. & Levanidov, L. Ya. (1973). Effects of manganese trace element fertilizers on the composition of polyphenolic compounds of *Rumex tianschanicus*. *Uspevaemostj izuch. lek. rastenij Sib., Materialia Mezhvuz.* Konferentia 1973, pp. 93–4.

Peterson, P. J. (1969). The distribution of zinc-65 in *Agrostis tenuis* Sibth. and *A. stolonifera* L. tissues. *Journal of Experimental Botany* **20**, 863–75.

Reilly, C. (1972). Amino acids and amino acid–copper complexes in water-soluble extracts of copper-tolerant and non-tolerant *Becium homblei*. *Zeitschrift für Pflanzenphysiologie* **66**, 294–6.

Reilly, A. & Reilly, C. (1973). Zinc, lead and copper tolerance in the grass *Stereochlaena cameronii* (Stapf) Clayton. *New Phytologist* **72**, 1041–6.

Reilly, C., Rowel, J. & Stone, J. (1970). The accumulation and binding of copper in leaf tissue of *Becium homblei* (DeWild.) Duvign. & Plancke. *New Phytologist* **69**, 993–7.

Schiller, W. (1974). Versuche zur Kupferresistenz bei Schwermetallökotypen von *Silene cucubalus* Wib. *Flora, Jena* **163**, 327–41.

Seno, T. (1963). Genetic relationship between brown colouration and copper resistance in *Saccharomyces cerevisiae*. *Memoirs of the College of Science, Kyoto University*, Ser. B **30**, 1–8.

Shank, K. E. & Vetter, R. J. (1974). Effects of copper, mercury, and zinc on the uptake and distribution of cadmium-115 in the albino rat. *Environmental Letters* **6**, 13–18.

Sillen, L. G. & Martell, A. E. (1964). *Stability constants of metal ion complexes.* Chemical Society, London. 754 pp.

Somers, E. (1963). The uptake of copper by fungal cells. *Annals of Applied Biology* **51**, 425–37.

Steenken, F. (1973). Fumigation of cultivated plants with lead-containing and lead-free automobile exhaust gases. *Zeitschrift für Pflanzenkrankeiten und Pflanzenschutz* **80**, 513–27.

Suchodoller, A. (1967). Untersuchungen über den Bleigehalt von Pflanzen in der Nähe von Strassen und über die Bleiaufnahme und Translokation durch Pflanzen. *Berichte der Schweizerischen Botanischen Gesellschaft* **77**, 266–308.

Tokuyama, T. & Asano, K. (1974). Copper ion resistant bacteria. II. Distribution of copper in the cells of *Pseudomonas* species No. 20A. *Nihon Daigaku Nojuigakubu Gakajutsu Kenkyu Hokoku* **31**, 203–13.

Tornabene, T. G. & Edwards, H. W. (1972). Microbial uptake of lead. *Science* **176**, 1334–5.

Turner, R. G. (1969). Heavy metal tolerance in plants. In *Ecological aspects of the mineral nutrition in plants. British Ecological Society Symposium, 1968,* Ed. I. H. Rorison, pp. 399–410. Blackwell Scientific Publications, Oxford.

Turner, R. G. (1970). The subcellular distribution of zinc and copper within the roots of metal tolerant clones of *Agrostis tenuis* Sibth. *New Phytologist* **69**, 725–31.

Turner, R. G. & Gregory, R. P. G. (1967). The use of radioisotopes to investigate heavy metal tolerances in plants. In *Isotopes in plant nutrition and physiology*, pp. 493–509. IAEA/FAO, Vienna.

Turner, R. G. & Marshall, C. (1972). The accumulation of zinc by subcellular fractions of roots of *Agrostis tenuis* Sibth. in relation to zinc tolerance. *New Phytologist* **71**, 671–6.

Uchida, Y., Saito, Y., Kaziwara, H. & Enomoto, H. (1973). Cadmium resistant microorganisms. I. Isolation of cadmium-resistant bacteria and the uptake of cadmium by these organisms. *Saga Daigaku Nogaku Iho* **35**, 15–24.

Valee, B. L. & Ulmer, D. D. (1972). Biochemical effects of mercury, cadmium and lead. *Annual Review of Biochemistry* **41**, 91–128.

Venkateswerlu, G. & Sivarama Sastry, K. (1970). The mechanism of uptake of cobalt ions by *Neurospora crassa*. *Biochemical Journal* **118**, 497–503.

Vetter, H. & Mählhop, R. (1971). Untersuchungen über Blei-, Zinkund Fluor-Immissionen und dadurch verursachte Schäden an Pflanzen und Tieren. *Landwirtschaftliche Forschung* **24**, 294–315.

Wagner, K. H. & Siddiqui, I. (1973). Schwermetallkontamination durch industrielle Immissionen-Untersuchungen an Boden, Futterpflanzen und Rinderlebern aus dem Raum Nordenham. *Naturwissenschaften* **60**, 161.

Wakiuchi, N., Matsumoto, H. & Takahashi, E. (1971). Changes of some enzyme activities of cucumber during ammonium toxicity. *Physiologia Plantarum* **24**, 248–53.

Welch, W. R. & Dick, D. L. (1975). Lead concentration in tissues of roadside mice. *Environmental Pollution* **8**, 15–21.

Wild, H. (1974). The vegetation of arsenical soils. *Kirkia* **9**, 243–64.

Willert, D. J. von (1974). Der Einfluss von NaCl auf die Atmung und Aktivität der Malatdehydrogenase bei einigen Halophyten und Glykophyten. *Oecologia, Berlin* **14**, 127–37.

Woolhouse, H. W. (1970). Environment and enzyme evolution in plants. In *Phytochemical phylogeny*, Ed. J. B. Harborne, pp. 207–31. Academic Press, New York & London.

Wu, L. & Bradshaw, A. D. (1972). Aerial pollution and the rapid evolution of copper tolerance. *Nature, London* **238**, 167–9.

A.D.BRADSHAW

Pollution and evolution

Pollution is itself an environmental change. As such it might well be expected to cause evolutionary changes in the plant and animal populations being affected. An environmental change means new selection pressures, which, if there is heritable variation present, must cause changes in gene frequency and therefore changes in the genetic make-up of the populations involved.

All this is easy to appreciate. Indeed the best examples of evolutionary changes in plants are in populations in new environments (Bradshaw, 1972). However in most experimental studies on the effects of pollutants great care is taken to keep the genetic constitution of the organism constant and vary only the pollutant and other physical factors. So it is not inappropriate in this volume to consider what can happen in polluted situations to the population rather than to the individual.

Variability and pollution

Without the appropriate variability evolution cannot occur. Homozygous, genetically pure varieties of crop plants produced by continued inbreeding can be grown in a wide variety of habitats for many years without any genetic change occurring, in total contrast to the heterozygous, variable varieties of outbred crop plants which can change very rapidly. Yet in outbred plants as well as inbred there can often be a deficiency of the genes for a desirable character, which means that the plant breeder may have to go to elaborate ends to extract them from another source.

Does this mean that in many cases there is little variability available in plant populations of adaptive significance to pollution? For the most part polluted situations are new situations. As a result the gene pools of the species concerned are in effect unselected in relation to the pollution factor. In this case they might be expected to show a wide range of relevant variability, even although with regard to more normal environmental factors, to which they will have been subjected for long periods of time, they will show much less variability due to the combined effects of stabilising and directional selection. Extensive hidden variability, only apparent in populations in relation to factors to which they have not been subjected previously, has been well demonstrated by Cooper (1954).

Whether such variability exists in relation to pollution factors has never been systematically examined except in cases which will be discussed later. But there is widespread general evidence of genetic variation in response to pollutants (Table 1). The most significant is the variation found within species: this ranges from individual genotypes of wild or cultivated plants which have been discovered to have particular sensitivity or resistance to pollution, to natural populations found growing in polluted areas which have evolved tolerance to the pollution factor concerned. The evidence of differences in sensitivity to pollution factors found between species is, however, also important, since species differences are determined by genetic differences. But such differences may only be the incidental outcome of major

Table 1. *Types of genetical variation in response to pollutants*

	Between genotypes	Between populations	Between species
Usual occurrence	At random within any populations of cultivated or wild plants, including differences between homozygous or vegetative varieties	In those populations subject to selection in polluted areas	At random, unless in relation to a natural pollution factor
Usual cause	Variation due to mutation and segregation	Systematic differences in gene frequency due to selection	Fortuitous characteristic, or side-effect of adaptation to other factors, unless in relation to a natural pollution factor
Notable examples	Susceptibility of Bel W_3 tobacco to ozone (Heggestad & Menser, 1962); resistance of different ryegrass genotypes to herbicides (Wright, 1966); different sensitivities of *Gladiolus* varieties to fluoride (Hitchcock, Zimmerman & Coe, 1962)	Heavy metal tolerance in populations of many species (Antonovics, Bradshaw & Turner, 1971); tolerance of Helmshore ryegrass to sulphur dioxide (Bell & Clough, 1973); tolerance of Glasgow populations of *Marchantia* to lead (Briggs, 1972)	Different sensitivities of lichens to sulphur dioxide (Gilbert, 1970); sensitivities of a wide range of species to sulphur dioxide (O'Gara, 1956); adaptation of *Ulva lactuca* to exploit high ammonium (Waite & Gregory, 1969)

differences in physiology and morphology which have no direct relation to pollution, such as the greater sensitivity of conifers to sulphur dioxide pollution which can be attributed to their evergreen habit.

The variation between genotypes is the raw material on which selection can act. In this respect it represents the potential for evolution rather than the outcome of evolution. This does not in any way deny its importance, as will be discussed later, but it does suggest that the most valuable evidence on the degree to which evolution in relation to pollution can take place is that provided by populations growing in polluted areas found to be resistant to the pollution they have endured.

In plants there is now evidence of populations showing specific adaptation to most known pollutants, and now even to pollutants which have only been in existence for a few years, such as lead from car exhausts (populations of *Marchantia polymorpha* in Glasgow; Briggs, 1972), triazine herbicides used in weed control (population of *Senecio vulgaris* in USA; Ryan, 1970) and heavy metals from a new refining industry (populations of six different grass species in Uganda; Edroma, 1974): such rapidity is quite remarkable.

It is easy to appreciate the possibility of evolution of populations adapted to pollutants which have severe effects. There are, however, many pollutants which in their normal concentrations have only slight, but chronic, effects: the most notable is sulphur dioxide. Such pollutants might be considered to have no evolutionary effects at all. The existence of the Helmshore population of *Lolium perenne*, whose properties have been described in an earlier paper in this volume and previously (Bell & Clough, 1973), is therefore remarkable from an evolutionary point of view. Not only does it show that *Lolium perenne* has the capacity to evolve tolerance to sulphur dioxide, but also that it can do so in levels of sulphur dioxide which up to now have not been considered to be serious. It therefore follows that the sulphur dioxide levels in Lancashire must have been sufficiently debilitating to normal *Lolium* to cause the selection of a resistant population. Since *Lolium* is a very important herbage grass a deduction, which is subsidiary to the subject of this volume but which is of considerable general significance, is that the effects of sulphur dioxide in rural areas can hardly be dismissed as being unimportant (Bradshaw, 1973).

Heavy metal tolerance

One of the best-known examples of evolution in relation to pollution is in relation to heavy metal pollution: it was also the earliest to be discovered (Prat, 1934). It is a clear-cut case where the pollutant causes the evolution of local, adapted populations; there is no indication so far of species with pre-existing tolerance occurring throughout their range of distribution. Heavy metals are easy to handle experimentally, and tolerance can easily be tested by an examination of root growth: it can be quantified by a comparison of root growth in the presence of metal with growth in its absence. At the same time sources of pollution are widespread and tolerance has evolved in a large number of species. As a result a great deal of work has been carried out in the past two decades which gives us a very solid picture of the evolutionary processes involved (for general review see Antonovics, Bradshaw & Turner, 1971), which can be applied to other pollution situations. For this reason the rest of this paper is devoted to an analysis of these evolutionary processes.

Adapted populations must possess a mechanism for coping with the pollution factor, and this mechanism must have a proper genetic basis.

There are many different mechanisms by which a plant can withstand pollution:

(a) exclusion of the pollutant by modifications to cuticles, stomata, or uptake mechanisms etc.;

(b) complexing of the pollutant internally in such a way as to render it unchanged but innocuous;

(c) degradation of the pollutant to innocuous by-products;

(d) development of resistant enzymes which can function in elevated internal levels of the pollutant.

In metal-tolerant plants the main mechanisms appear to be the development of complexing systems of considerable specificity such as those discussed by Ernst earlier in this volume. In *Agrostis tenuis* the main site of complexing is in the cell wall (Turner & Marshall, 1972). The result of this

Table 2.   *Analysis of variance: 10 × 10 diallel analysis of* Anthoxanthum odoratum

Components	Degrees of freedom (d.f.)	Sum of squares (s.s.)	Mean square (m.s.)	Variance ratio (v.r.)	Probability (P)
Additive	9	27 726.0	3080.6	255.0	0.1%
Dominance	45	6 273.0	139.4	11.5	0.1%
Material	9	66.5	7.4	0.6	n.s.
Reciprocal	36	548.5	15.2	1.3	n.s.
Error	100	1 054.0	12.1		

After Gartside & McNeilly (1974a).

in copper-tolerant material is that copper accumulates in the roots and does not pass up readily into the upper parts of the plant: this is in complete contrast to normal material (Wu, Thurman & Bradshaw, 1975) (Fig. 1).

The existence of tolerant populations whose characteristics are not altered in cultivation is itself evidence of genetic control of tolerance. Better evidence

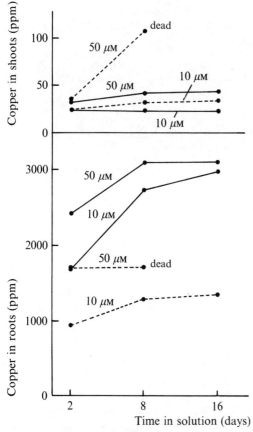

Fig. 1.   The uptake of copper by tolerant (solid lines) and non-tolerant (dashed lines) clones of *Agrostis stolonifera*. (After Wu, Thurman & Bradshaw, 1975.)

is when it can be shown that tolerance is passed on to offspring. Parent/ offspring regressions have been determined indicating that copper tolerance has a high heritability (McNeilly & Bradshaw, 1968). A more detailed study of zinc tolerance in *Anthoxanthum odoratum* using a diallel analysis shows that the character has high heritability and is determined by more than one pair of alleles with partial dominance of tolerance (Gartside & McNeilly, 1974a). The relevant analysis is given in Table 2. This substantiates earlier

Fig. 2. *Festuca rubra* populations on a zinc- and lead-polluted site 3 years after sowing. Left, normal non-tolerant population; right, zinc- and lead-tolerant population.

work on other species such as *Silene vulgaris* (Broker, 1963) and *Festuca rubra* (Urquhart, 1971). Metal tolerance therefore behaves genetically like most other ordinary characters.

The changes determined by selection

Given suitable heritable variation in the base population it is obvious that selection due to the pollution factor must be the prime force causing evolutionary change. Differential fitness of different genotypes in polluted conditions, which can most easily be determined by measurement of total growth, provides direct evidence of the power of selection. In metal contaminated situations normal genotypes usually have fitnesses of zero compared with their fitnesses in uncontaminated situations, and genotypes which are tolerant have fitnesses between 0.5 and 1 depending on the toxicity of the pollutant. Differential selection in favour of tolerant genotypes can therefore be very powerful indeed (Fig. 2). It has been suggested that this would be quite sufficient to cause the rapid changes that appear to have occurred in plant populations, for instance the evolution of zinc tolerance under a zinc-coated wire fence in 25 years (Snaydon; in Bradshaw, McNeilly & Gregory, 1965).

Recently the rapidity with which selection can occur in plant populations has been analysed by some simple experiments involving the sowing of seed of normal populations of *Agrostis tenuis* on metal-contaminated soil (Walley, Khan & Bradshaw, 1974). Although nearly all seeds germinate, at the end of 6–8 months only very few individuals survive and grow reasonably (about 2%). This can be expressed in terms of plant height at the end of the experiment (Fig. 3); only those seedlings more than 50 mm high were alive.

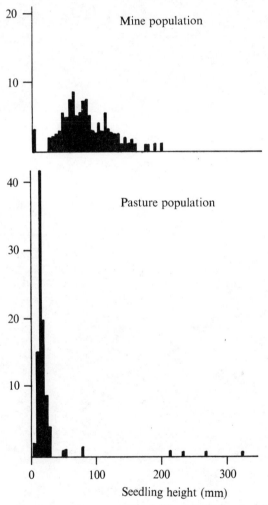

Fig. 3.   Frequency distribution of height of seedlings of a sample of non-tolerant *Agrostis tenuis* after growth on slightly ameliorated copper waste for a period of 4 months. (After Walley, Khan & Bradshaw, 1974.)

Fig. 4.   The effects of aerial copper pollution near Liverpool. (a) Railway
embankment away from source, with diversity of species; (b) railway
embankment near source with no plants visible, except odd plants
of copper-tolerant *Agrostis stolonifera* between the railway lines.

The survivors all showed significant metal tolerance, the degree of tolerance correlating with plant height. The tolerance approached that of populations long-established in polluted areas, and suggested that fully tolerant populations could be evolved in only one or two generations of selection, which in a natural situation would require just a few years.

A copper-contaminated site outside Liverpool has provided the opportunity to test this suggestion (Wu, Bradshaw & Thurman, 1975). Around a copper refinery there are large areas denuded of vegetation by high levels of copper pollution giving soil levels of over 2000 $\mu g\ g^{-1}$ (Fig. 4). But within the polluted area there are a number of lawns of different ages composed almost entirely of *Agrostis stolonifera* and *A. tenuis*. The youngest lawns are a patchwork of isolated individuals with bare ground between; the oldest lawns have an excellent continuous plant cover despite high copper levels. Determinations of copper tolerance of individuals of *Agrostis stolonifera* taken from the lawns shows that there is a progressive build-up of tolerance in the populations; the non-tolerant individuals have been rapidly eliminated, and strongly tolerant individuals have been progressively selected (Fig. 5). Changes in the genetic structure of the populations are detectable in the youngest populations, and a lawn capable of growing satisfactorily on the polluted soil is evolved in 10 to 15 years. This represents the time taken for the selected tolerant individuals to produce a complete ground cover, and probably for a second generation to develop.

The selection takes place both at the seedling and the adult stages. Among the generally tolerant individuals which survive the seedling phase there is selection of the most tolerant by their more vigorous vegetative growth (*Agrostis stolonifera* is a perennial). But this does not mean that the populations are ultimately composed of only a few highly successful individual genotypes (clones). Studies of esterase isoenzyme variation between individuals show that the lawns consist of a large number of distinct genotypes.

It is likely that exactly the same processes occur on the bottoms of ships which have been treated with copper antifouling paint, although whether ship owners would like to consider the hulls of their ships polluted is another matter. Not long after treatment the hulls become colonised with the alga *Ectocarpus siliculosus*. The populations which colonise are copper-tolerant whereas normal populations are not (Russell & Morris, 1970, 1973) (Fig. 6). The fouling only occurs as a result of the evolution of tolerance which arises from the selection of the rare tolerant individuals which occur in normal populations (Fig. 7). The breeding system of *Ectocarpus siliculosus* is not fully understood. It is possible that no sexual generations are involved and we have a simple one-step process of evolution. Even if this is so the products

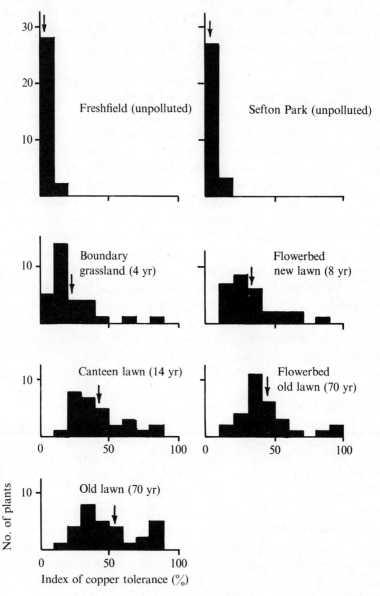

Fig. 5.   The distribution of copper tolerance in populations of different ages around a copper refinery near Liverpool. Arrows indicate mean values. (After Wu, Bradshaw & Thurman, 1975.)

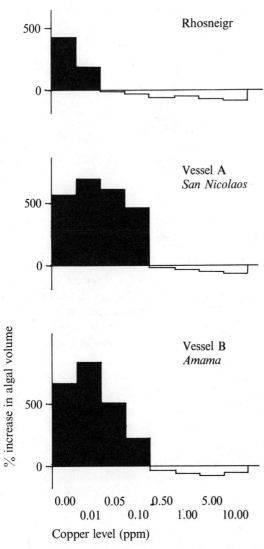

Fig. 6.   The growth at different copper levels of populations of *Ectocarpus siliculosus* from the hulls of two ships and from Rhosneigr, an unpolluted environment. (After Russell & Morris, 1970.)

are of considerable economic disadvantage since the ship-fouling they cause can add several thousands of pounds to the costs of a single voyage.

Polluted situations therefore provide very powerful selection, which can very rapidly change the genetic constitution of the populations affected.

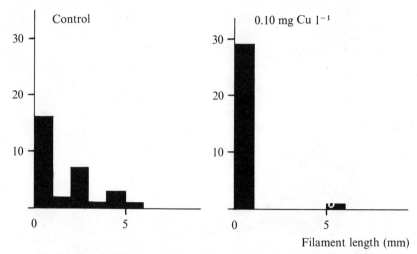

Fig. 7.   The distribution of growth in a copper-containing medium of individual sporelings of *Ectocarpus siliculosus* from a single unpolluted population compared with the growth in a control medium containing no copper. (After Russell & Morris, 1973.)

The rate of change will depend on the rate of growth of the selected tolerant individuals and their reproductive abilities. Perennial plants, even if they reproduce in their second year and have strong vegetative reproduction, may take several years to form a large tolerant population. Annual plants may take fewer years. Organisms such as *Ectocarpus* which take only a few weeks from germination to the discharge of spores can probably build up large tolerant populations in only a few months, perhaps during a single voyage.

The control exercised by variability

Evolution, however, depends on the presence of the appropriate variability on which selection can act. At the outset it was suggested that evolution in relation to pollution is widespread, particularly in cases involving heavy metals. This is true on a worldwide scale; there are twenty-one species listed by Antonovics *et al.* (1971) in which the occurrence of metal tolerant populations has been demonstrated and there must be many more species in which tolerance must occur, since another fifty-five species are specifically listed as indicators of metal-contaminated soils, and there is a very large number of other species known to occur on these soils.

But in any metal-polluted situation the first and most obvious characteristic of the flora is that it is reduced to a few species. In the copper-contaminated site near Liverpool only two species of flowering plant are found in the lawns; *Agrostis tenuis* and *A. stolonifera*. Yet in the surrounding area there are at least fifty species to be found in lawns. There is no obvious reason attributable to selection as to why so many species are missing. The pollution is aerial and the copper widely distributed, so all species have had equal opportunities to be influenced by selection.

The most likely explanation for the exclusion of some species is that they do not possess the necessary variability (Khan, 1969, in Bradshaw, 1971). Gartside & McNeilly (1974b) therefore examined the occurrence, using the seedling selection technique, of copper tolerance in populations of a number of grassland species which are not to be found in copper-contaminated sites, as well in a normal population of *Agrostis tenuis*, a species which we already

Table 3. *Variability in copper tolerance available for selection in different grass species determined by screening normal populations by growth on mine soils*

Species	Survivors per 5000 plants		Copper tolerance (%)		
	On mine soil	On ameliorated mine soil	Five best survivors	Five best offspring	Unselected material
Found on copper waste					
Agrostis tenuis	2	4	55	35	6
Not found on copper waste					
Arrhenatherum elatius	0	4	8	6	0
Poa trivialis	0	2	5		0
Cynosurus cristatus	0	2	6		0
Lolium perenne	0	5	11	9	0
Dactylis glomerata	0	6	48	43	5

After Gartside & McNeilly (1974b and personal communication).

know to possess variability in copper tolerance which can be selected. The results, summarised in Table 3, show that the species fall into three groups; (i) those that produce no survivors at all; (ii) those that produce survivors whose offspring are not tolerant; and (iii) *Agrostis tenuis* and *Dactylis glomerata* which produce survivors which give tolerant offspring. Except for *Dactylis glomerata* it is clear that species which do not grow in copper-contaminated areas do not possess the heritable variability enabling them to evolve tolerant populations. *Dactylis glomerata* is an anomaly since careful search has failed to find it so far on copper-contaminated sites: perhaps it is unable to evolve tolerance to some other attribute of the polluted site, such as low phosphate availability brought about by the presence of copper.

Apart from *Dactylis* the importance of variability in determining the amount of possible evolution is very clear, an observation with which all plant breeders will agree. In ecological and physiological terms it means that the ecological amplitude of a species is being determined by its genetical variability.

Fitness

We have already seen the considerable differences in the relative fitnesses of tolerant and non-tolerant genotypes in polluted situations. What is the difference in their fitnesses in normal situations? Does the possession of tolerance involve a requirement for the metal concerned, or a diversion of metabolites to the complexing mechanism, or tolerant enzymes with an inefficient function, so that the tolerant genotypes are at a disadvantage in normal situations?

The general evidence is that the fitness of tolerant genotypes when grown in normal soils is little different from normal genotypes. This is particularly so in *Agrostis tenuis* (McNeilly, 1966). But there are cases where tolerant genotypes are distinctly less fit, for example zinc-tolerant *Anthoxanthum odoratum* (Antonovics & Bradshaw, 1970): an extreme case is that of zinc-tolerant *Armeria maritima* which will not grow in normal soils without the application of zinc (Lefébvre, in Antonovics, Bradshaw & Turner, 1971). An indication of a requirement for particular metals by tolerant material comes from indices of metal tolerance of more than 100%, which indicate that root growth is better in the presence of the metal than in its absence (Table 4).

But the ultimate fitness of a genotype cannot be tested by its growth in isolation. It must be tested under the conditions of competition with other species which it will inevitably meet in normal situations. Under these conditions the fitness of tolerant genotypes of a range of species relative to those of normal genotypes is considerably reduced (Cook, Lefébvre & McNeilly, 1972; Hickey & McNeilly, 1976). Furthermore in perennial plants

Table 4. *Species showing an index of tolerance indicative of root growth being stimulated by presence of metal ions in the testing solution*

Species	Metal	Reference
Agrostis tenuis	Copper	McNeilly (1968)
	Lead	Jowett (1964)
	Lead, copper, zinc	Barker (1967)
Mimulus guttatus	Copper	Allen & Sheppard (1971)
Anthoxanthum odoratum	Zinc	Putwain (1963)
		Antonovics (1966)
		Gadgil (1969)
Holcus lanatus	Zinc	Jenkins & Winfield (1964)
Armeria maritima	Zinc	Lefébvre (1969)

After Antonovics, Bradshaw & Turner (1971). Details of the references cited in the table are given in this paper.

the effects of adverse factors are cumulative, so that relative fitnesses decline rapidly with time to low levels (Fig. 8).

This means that in the absence of pollution there is strong selection against tolerance. In this case, when pollution declines the tolerant populations involved ought to change in gene frequency back towards their original

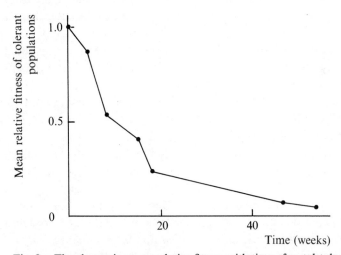

Fig. 8. The change in mean relative fitness with time of metal-tolerant populations of four species (*Agrostis tenuis, Anthoxanthum odoratum, Plantago lanceolata* and *Rumex acetosa*), in competition with *Lolium perenne*. Relative fitness is measured as growth of tolerant population in competition/growth of non-tolerant population in competition. (After Hickey & McNeilly, 1976.)

state. This has not been shown for plants, but a reduction in the frequency of melanics in populations of *Biston betularia* (peppered moth) around Manchester in response to smoke control has recently been reported (Cook, Askew & Bishop, 1970).

The relative fitness of the sulphur dioxide tolerant Helmshore population of *Lolium perenne* in the absence of sulphur dioxide but in the presence of competition needs determining. In the absence of competition the tolerant material does not appear less fit than normal material. If the tolerant material is less fit in the presence of competition then it should be eliminated when sulphur dioxide levels decline. Sulphur dioxide emissions have generally been reduced, yet very tolerant material continues to be found at Helmshore. This suggests that there has not been any effective reduction in biologically significant sulphur dioxide levels in the Helmshore area. This fits in with the limited data for sulphur dioxide levels presented by Bell & Mudd (see p. 90).

Evolutionary equilibria

This analysis of the balance of selective forces indicates an evolutionary equilibrium determined by selection. This indeed must always exist. In polluted situations there is, however, an extra factor making the equilibrium of factors determining the gene frequencies, and therefore the characteristics of polluted populations, even more finely balanced. This factor is gene flow, by the movement of pollen and seeds from neighbouring normal populations, which tends to drown the characteristics of the tolerant populations. It arises because pollution, particularly by heavy metals, so often occurs in small areas, and the tolerant populations which evolve are therefore more likely to be subject to an influx of alien genes from surrounding normal populations of the same species.

In a single population on a small contaminated area the effects of gene flow can easily be seen by a comparison of the tolerance of the adult plants actually growing on the area with the tolerance of the seed they produce *in situ* and in isolation (McNeilly, 1966; McNeilly & Bradshaw, 1968) (Fig. 9). There is a considerable lowering in the tolerance of the seed produced *in situ* which must be due to the influx of alien non-tolerant genes. But this influx of alien genes must be being kept in check by selection because the adult population is tolerant. The strong selection pressures for tolerance we have already discussed will ensure this. Similarly the movement of genes out of the population into normal populations will be kept in check by selection against tolerance.

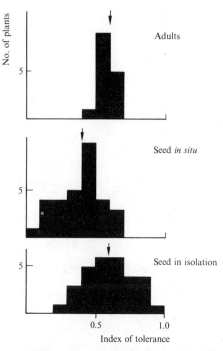

Fig. 9.   The distribution of copper tolerance in an adult, copper mine population of *Agrostis tenuis* compared with that in the seed produced by the same population *in situ* and in isolation. Arrows indicate mean values. (After McNeilly, 1966.)

Gene flow by pollen has a distribution with high values over short distances, then a sharp fall to low values which persist over longer distances. This means that mean pollen movement is little. Gene flow is reduced if a population is aggregated into clumps or is at high density (Gleaves, 1973). So in practice gene flow does not usually appear to over-ride selection and even very small polluted areas evolve tolerant populations (McNeilly, 1968). This localised evolution is aided by perenniality since once a few tolerant plants become established in a polluted area gene flow is effectively at an end. This presumably is the explanation of the occurrence of zinc tolerance under a zinc-coated wire fence found by Snaydon (Bradshaw, McNeilly & Gregory, 1965).

By the same arguments, the characteristics of populations at the boundary between a polluted and an unpolluted area should change very sharply in relation to pollution levels. This is indeed found (Jain & Bradshaw, 1966) (*Anthoxanthum odoratum* in Fig. 10). But the sharpness of the change should relate to the fitness of the genotypes in the environments concerned, since

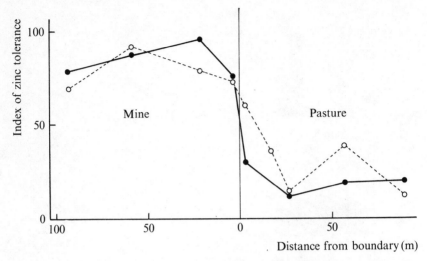

Fig. 10.   The zinc tolerance of populations of *Anthoxanthum odoratum* (●)
and *Agrostis tenuis* (○) at the mine boundary at Trelogan, North Wales.
All *Agrostis* values have been multiplied by three. (After Hickey
& McNeilly, 1976).

these fitnesses determine the selection which maintains the distinctiveness
of the subpopulations on the two sides of the boundary. There is evidence
that the fitness of tolerant genotypes, measured in competition in normal
situations, varies between species; the fitness of tolerant *Anthoxanthum
odoratum* is much lower than that of tolerant *Agrostis tenuis* (Hickey &
McNeilly, 1976) (Table 5). Thus the gradient of change in zinc tolerance of
Agrostis tenuis across the boundary between polluted and unpolluted areas

Table 5.   *Relative fitnesses* of metal-tolerant populations of four
species when in competition with ryegrass* (Lolium perenne)

| | Ryegrass variety acting as competitor | |
	S23 (pasture type)	S24 (hay type)
Agrostis tenuis	0.32	0.16
Anthoxanthum odoratum	0.03	0.001
Plantago lanceolata	0.03	0.28
Rumex acetosa	0.27	0.23

After Hickey & McNeilly (1976).

* Expressed as $\dfrac{\text{mean yield of tolerant population}}{\text{mean yield of non-tolerant population}}$.

at Trelogan mine appears to be less than that of *Anthoxanthum odoratum* (Fig. 10).

For the same reason in an area of widespread pollution such as at Parys Mountain in Anglesey the characteristics of populations of a species such as *Agrostis tenuis* may come to resemble one another, and populations growing on unpolluted sites in the area may be more tolerant than would be expected (S. Karataglis, personal communication) (Fig. 11). Selection against tolerance in uncontaminated areas is not sufficient to overcome gene flow.

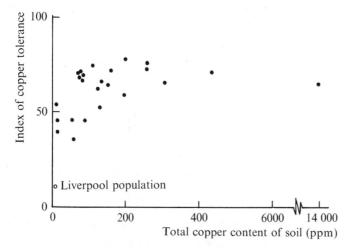

Fig. 11.   The copper tolerance of populations of *Agrostis tenuis* from the copper mining area of Parys Mountain, Anglesey, and from a normal soil in Liverpool, in relation to the copper content of their soils. (S. Karataglis, personal communication.)

The amount of gene flow rather than the severity of selection can affect the pattern of differentiation of populations in a similar manner. Where there is strong gene flow due to a polarised wind direction there can be a greater spilling-over of tolerant genes into neighbouring non-tolerant populations (McNeilly, 1968) (Fig. 12). In animal species where differences in amount of movement can arise due to behavioural differences, very considerable differences in patterns of differentiation can be found, as in the occurrence of melanism in the Liverpool region in the moths *Biston betularia* and *Gonodontis bidentata*. *Biston* is very mobile and has a less localised pattern of differentiation (Bishop & Cook, 1975) than *Gonodontis*.

It is easy to think that gene flow has only rather deleterious effects, undermining the adaptation of populations. But it has the important effect of distributing genes over long distances. This is particularly true in situations

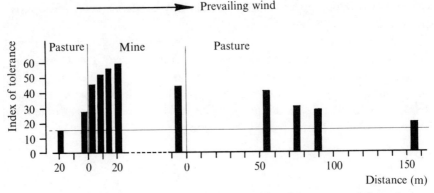

Fig. 12.   The copper tolerance of populations of *Agrostis tenuis* from the up-wind and down-wind areas of the copper mine at Drws-y-Coed, North Wales. (After McNeilly, 1968.)

where there is a continuous chain of populations away from a polluted site. Despite selection against genes for tolerance in unpolluted areas, genes for tolerance will be maintained in populations a long distance from the polluted tolerant population (Gleaves, 1973 and personal communication). This can be seen by the occurrence of copper tolerance in seed sampled from populations of *Agrostis tenuis* several kilometres away from the copper mine at Parys Mountain (Khan, in Bradshaw, 1971) (Fig. 13). If new areas of copper pollution arose around the Parys Mountain area an adequate supply of

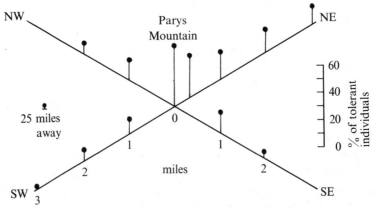

Fig. 13.   The occurrence of tolerant individuals in seed samples of *Agrostis tenuis* in populations in the region around Parys Mountain, Anglesey. Numbers show distance from Parys Mountain in miles. (After Khan, in Bradshaw, 1971.)

genes would be available to ensure the rapid evolution of a tolerant population.

Conclusions

Evolution in relation to pollution is widespread and is found in many plant species and in relation to many different pollutants. This sort of evolution is only to be expected; indeed it is inevitable, if variability in resistance to pollution is present in normal populations, because of the selection pressures that can be developed by pollution factors.

Also there is evidence that such evolution can be extremely rapid. If the cases had been reported a few years ago we might well have dismissed them as arising from faulty observation. But now we can see that they are the expected outcome of very high selection pressures. As a result population changes must be always considered as a likely occurrence in pollution situations. Their occurrence must be taken into account in the analysis of pollution episodes, and in forecasts of the probable effects of pollutants.

The evolution of populations resistant to pollution enables species which would otherwise be eliminated to persist in polluted situations. This represents an increase in the ecological amplitude of the species which cannot be forecast from studies of the mean behaviour of the original populations. Although this might be forecast from the behaviour of particular, rare individuals, it would be very difficult to forecast in practice because of the rarity of tolerant individuals in normal populations and the likelihood that it would take a few generations to achieve the maximum level of tolerance.

The ability of tolerant populations to persist in polluted situations must not be underestimated. In the case of metal tolerance the possession of tolerance confers on the population the ability to survive and grow well in conditions which eliminate the normal populations. This ability is being exploited to produce material which can be used to stabilise metalliferous waste heaps and reduce pollution (Smith & Bradshaw, 1972). There is no doubt that other material could be found for use in other polluted situations. This approach is particularly valuable where the pollutant cannot be reduced or eliminated.

In existing polluted situations the tolerant populations of those species which can evolve tolerance contribute considerably to the naturally occurring flora. Without the evolution of tolerance such a flora would not exist. It is interesting, therefore, to discover that the restricted nature of the flora seems to be explained by the occurrence or lack of the appropriate variation. In predicting what might occur in a polluted situation it is therefore worthwhile to carry out screening experiments to get an indication of the potential for evolutionary change shown by the base populations. Account will need to be taken of the life history of the species concerned, because species with short life cycles and strong reproductive powers will be able to respond more rapidly than those with long life cycles. Species such as trees will be the extreme: they will hardly be able to respond at all in the short-term, although in the long-term there is no doubt that they can evolve populations as tolerant of extreme conditions as other species.

Evolution in a pollution situation is influenced by a variety of factors, as this paper has endeavoured to show. The interaction of these factors provides elegant evidence for the complexity of evolution which is of great theoretical interest. But the over-riding practical fact is that the evolution does occur, can be extremely rapid, and can substantially alter the response of species to the effects of pollution.

I owe a great debt of gratitude to all those whose results I have used. I am particularly grateful to Dr T. McNeilly, Mr T. Gleaves, Mr D. Hickey and Mr S. Karataglis for letting me use their unpublished data.

Summary

There is now widespread evidence of evolution in relation to pollution factors. It is a phenomenon that can no longer be disregarded in pollution situations. It can occur rapidly, and in relation to both acute and chronic pollution.

A model of what can occur is provided by the evidence on evolution in relation to heavy metal contamination.

This shows that the action of natural selection directly determines the outcome, by rapidly eliminating all those individuals except the most tolerant. As a result full tolerance can evolve in only one or two generations.

However ultimate control is exercised by the availability of appropriate variability. There are many species which do not evolve tolerance because they do not possess the necessary genetic variability in their base populations.

The pattern of differentiation is affected by other factors, especially the interaction between the relative fitness of tolerant and non-tolerant genotypes and the amount of gene flow between different populations. Usually the pattern of selection is the determinant and even very small polluted areas can have distinctive populations. But where the relative fitnesses of tolerant and non-tolerant genotypes are not very different, or there is high gene flow, the distinction between the populations occurring in neighbouring polluted and unpolluted areas can be reduced.

Evolution of tolerance to pollution factors is of considerable ecological significance because it allows a species which would otherwise be eliminated, to survive in a polluted situation.

References

Antonovics, J. & Bradshaw, A. D. (1970). Evolution in closely adjacent plant populations. VIII. Clinal patterns in *Anthoxanthum odoratum* across a mine boundary. *Heredity* **25**, 349–62.

Antonovics, J., Bradshaw, A. D. & Turner, R. G. (1971). Heavy metal tolerance in plants. *Advances in Ecological Research* **7**, 1–85.

Bell, J. N. B. & Clough, W. S. (1973). Depression of yield in ryegrass exposed to sulphur dioxide. *Nature, London* **241**, 47–9.

Bishop, J. A. & Cook, L. M. (1975). Moths, melanism and clean air. *Scientific American* **232**, 90–9.

Bradshaw, A. D. (1971). Plant evolution in extreme environments. In *Ecological genetics and evolution*, Ed. R. Creed, pp. 20–50. Blackwell Scientific Publications, Oxford.

Bradshaw, A. D. (1972). Some of the evolutionary consequences of being a plant. *Evolutionary Biology* **5**, 25–47.

Bradshaw, A. D. (1973). The ecological effects of pollutants. In *Fuel and the environment* **1**, 129–34. Institute of Fuel, London.

Bradshaw, A. D., McNeilly, T. & Gregory, R. P. G. (1965). Industrialisation, evolution and the development of heavy metal tolerance in plants. In *Ecology and the industrial society. British Ecological Society Symposium* **5**, Ed. G. T. Goodman *et al.*, pp. 327–43. Blackwell Scientific Publications, Oxford.

Briggs, D. (1972). Population differentiation in *Marchantia polymorpha* in various lead pollution levels. *Nature, London* **238**, 166–7

Broker, W. (1963). Genetisch–physiologische Untersuchungen über die Zinkverträglichkeit von *Silene inflata* Sm. *Flora, Jena*, Ser. B **153**, 122–56.

Cook, L. M., Askew, R. R. & Bishop, J. A. (1970). Increasing frequency of the typical form of the peppered moth in Manchester. *Nature, London* **227**, 1155.

Cook, S. A., Lefébvre, C. & McNeilly, T. (1972). Competition between metal-tolerant and normal plant populations on normal soil. *Evolution* **26**, 355–72.

Cooper, J. P. (1954). Studies on growth and development in *Lolium*. IV. Genetic control of heading responses in local populations. *Journal of Ecology* **42**, 521–56.

Edroma, E. L. (1974). Copper pollution in Rwenzori National Park, Uganda. *Journal of Ecology* **11**, 1043–56.

Gartside, D. W. & McNeilly, T. (1974a). Genetic studies in heavy metal tolerant plants. I. Genetics of zinc tolerance in *Anthoxanthum odoratum*. *Heredity* **32**, 287–97.

158   A. D. BRADSHAW

Gartside, D. W. & McNeilly, T. (1974*b*). The potential for evolution of heavy metal tolerance in plants. II. Copper tolerance in normal populations of different plant species. *Heredity* **32**, 335–48.

Gilbert, O. L. (1970). Further studies on the effect of sulphur dioxide on lichens and bryophytes. *New Phytologist* **69**, 605–27.

Gleaves, J. T. (1973). Gene flow mediated by wind-borne pollen. *Heredity* **31**, 355–66.

Heggestad, H. E. & Menser, H. A. (1962). Leaf spot sensitive tobacco strain Bel-W3, a biological indicator of the air pollutant ozone. *Phytopathology* **52**, 735.

Hickey, D. A. & McNeilly, T. (1976). Competition between metal-tolerant and normal plant populations; a field experiment on normal soil. *Evolution*, in press.

Hitchcock, A. E. P., Zimmerman, P. W. & Coe, R. R. (1962). Results of ten years' work (1951–1960) on the effect of fluorides on gladiolus. *Contributions from the Boyce Thompson Institute* **21**, 303–44.

Jain, S. K. & Bradshaw, A. D. (1966). Evolutionary divergence among adjacent plant populations. I. The evidence and its theoretical analysis. *Heredity* **21**, 407–41.

McNeilly, T. (1966). The evolution of copper tolerance in *Agrostis*. PhD thesis, University of Wales.

McNeilly, T. (1968). Evolution in closely adjacent plant populations. III. *Agrostis tenuis* on a small copper mine. *Heredity* **23**, 99–108.

McNeilly, T. & Bradshaw, A. D. (1968). Evolutionary processes in populations of copper tolerant *Agrostis tenuis*, Sibth. *Evolution* **22**, 108–18.

O'Gara, P. J. (1956). Relative sensitivity of cultivated and native plants to injury by sulfur dioxide. Unpublished data. In *Air pollution handbook*, Ed. P. L. Magill, F. R. Holden & C. Ackley. McGraw-Hill, New York.

Prat, S. (1934). Die Erblichkeit der Resistenz gegen Kupfer. *Berichte der Deutschen botanischen Gesellschaft* **52**, 65–7.

Ryan, G. F. (1970). Resistance of common groundsel to simazine and atrazine. *Weed Science* **18**, 614–16.

Russell, G. & Morris, O. P. (1970). Copper tolerance in the marine fouling alga *Ectocarpus siliculosus*. *Nature, London* **228**, 288–9.

Russell, G. & Morris, O. P. (1973). Ship fouling as an evolutionary process. In *Proceedings of the III International Congress on Corrosion and Fouling, Washington*, pp. 719–30.

Smith, R. A. H. & Bradshaw, A. D. (1972). Stabilization of toxic mine wastes by the use of tolerant plant populations. *Transactions of the Institution of Mining and Metallurgy*, Ser. A **81**, 230–7.

Turner, R. G. & Marshall, C. (1972). The accumulation of zinc by subcellular fractions of roots of *Agrostis tenuis* Sibth., in relation to zinc tolerance. *New Phytologist* **71**, 671–6.

Urquhart, C. (1971). Genetics of lead tolerance in *Festuca ovina*. *Heredity* **26**, 19–33.

Waite, T. D. & Gregory, C. (1969). Notes on the growth of *Ulva* as a function of ammonia nitrogen. *Phytologia* **18**, 65–9.

Walley, K. A., Khan, M. S. I. & Bradshaw, A. D. (1974). The potential for evolution of heavy metal tolerance in plants. I. Copper and zinc tolerance in *Agrostis tenuis*. *Heredity* **32**, 309–19.

Wright, C. E. (1966). Some implications of genotype–herbicide interactions in the breeding of *Lolium perenne*. *Euphytica* **15**, 229–38.

Wu, Lin, Bradshaw, A. D. & Thurman, D. A. (1975). The potential for evolution of heavy metal tolerance in plants. III. The rapid evolution of copper tolerance in *Agrostis stolonifera*. *Heredity* **34**, 165–87.

Wu, Lin, Thurman, D. A. & Bradshaw, A. D. (1975). The uptake of copper and its effect on respiratory processes of roots of copper-tolerant and non-tolerant clones of *Agrostis stolonifera*. *New Phytologist* **75**, 225–9.

R.WILLIX

Appendix I. An introduction to the chemistry of atmospheric pollutants

Atmospheric pollutants span a diversity of emission types, and the discussion here will be mainly restricted to those commonly stemming from industrial processing and some types of power generation – namely nitrogen oxides, sulphur dioxide, carbon oxides, commoner hydrocarbons and ammonia. The increase in activity in both laboratory and field studies has produced many publications following on from the pioneering studies of Haagen-Smit[1] and Blacet[2] and the now classical text of Leighton[3].

Until quite recently the bulk of the effort in air pollution studies was expended in North America, and that in regions where solar radiation was a dominating influence. While sunlight is recognised as another physical ingredient, it will be considered here only where relevant. The extent of interaction among pollutants is dependent on both their chemical nature and quantity as well as such physical features as proximity to other sources, temperature, wind strength and direction, mixing depth, topography etc. Few of these physical factors will be considered here. This is essentially a review of thermal and photochemical processes in the lower atmosphere (with no sharp boundary but taken for convenience as < 20 km), extra-polating information derived from simulated conditions in the laboratory to gain an understanding of the atmospheric situation.†

Except in proximity to sources, air pollutant concentrations are some six orders of magnitude lower than the most abundant natural components of the atmosphere, and unless performed under such conditions, laboratory experiments can be uninformative if not actually misleading. There is no substitute for additional, corroborative analytical measurements in the field to give a fuller picture of the nature and quantity of primary emissions and their reaction products, from which an assessment of pollutant effects on human and animal welfare, damage to plants, material corrosion etc. may be made.

† See footnote page 162.

Primary pollutants

Sulphur dioxide

Because of its intrinsic interest to chemists and also because it is one of the more ubiquitous air pollutants, sulphur dioxide (SO_2) was one of the earliest pollutants to be studied. Norrish & Oldershaw[4] identified two bands in the near-ultraviolet absorption spectrum of SO_2, one commencing around 230 nm and stretching into the vacuum ultraviolet, the other between 390 nm and 250 nm.

$$\text{The process} \quad SO_2 \rightarrow SO + O \tag{1}$$

requires about 560 kJ mol^{-1} ($\simeq$ 6 eV molecule^{-1}) i.e. the wavelength 220 nm. The second absorption band (390–250 nm), which is of more relevance to atmospheric photochemistry, is unlikely to lead to the fragmentation described. The production of an electronically excited state of SO_2 is more probable:

$$SO_2 + h\nu \rightarrow SO_2{}^* \tag{2}$$

where h is Planck's constant, ν the frequency and the asterisk symbolises an excited state, i.e. a molecule possessing more energy than the unexcited or ground state, resulting in the promotion of electrons from one level to another.

It was suggested[5] early in the study of SO_2 that degradation of electronic

---

† For most of the reactions the rate constant, k, is quoted. This indicates the rate at which the reaction proceeds when the reactant concentrations are unity. Concentrations are expressed as moles litre^{-1} (symbol M or mol dm^{-3} in SI). Convenient conversions are:

(i) $M \times 24.45 \times 10^8$ = parts per hundred million (pphm).

(ii) For second-order rate constants
$$M^{-1} s^{-1} \times 2.46 \times 10^{-8} = pphm^{-1} min^{-1}$$
and $M^{-1} s^{-1} \times 1.47 \times 10^{-6} = pphm^{-1} h^{-1}$.

(iii) Concentrations are often quoted in $\mu g\ m^{-3}$.
These are converted to pphm as follows:

$$\text{quantity in } \mu g\ m^{-3} \times \frac{1}{\text{molecular weight (MW)} \times 10^6} \times 0.0244 \times 10^8$$

$$= \text{quantity in pphm};$$

or $pphm \times 10^{-2} \times MW \times 40.9 = \mu g\ m^{-3}$ (1 atmos pressure).

The enthalpy or heat change, ΔH, and the activation energy E_a are also quoted where appropriate. ΔH is connected with the feasibility of the process, negative values usually indicating a favoured reaction; and E_a the effect of temperature on rate. The significance of quoted values of k is that where k is 10^8 or greater in $M^{-1} s^{-1}$ units, reaction takes place at virtually every encounter. Values of temperature-dependent quantities are quoted for ~ 25 °C.

to thermal energy occurs by internal transit to a vibrationally excited ground state which may be dissipated by collision, rather than the electronic energy being lost by fluorescence of the excited molecule. The fact that products (e.g. sulphur trioxide, SO_3) are observed from the irradiation of SO_2 indicates that many molecules possess the additional energy for periods long enough for reaction to occur (although quantum yields[†] may be fairly small). The process

$$SO_2^* + SO_2 \rightarrow SO + SO_3 \tag{3}$$
$$\Delta H = -209 \text{ kJ mol}^{-1}$$

may be important near the point of emission of stack plumes but is unlikely to be significant in the diluted atmosphere where such collisions would be relatively infrequent.

Nevertheless in irradiated mixtures of SO_2/O_2 or $SO_2/$air, SO_2 loss does occur leading to SO_3 in dry systems or sulphuric acid in humid ones $(SO_3 + H_2O \rightarrow H_2SO_4)$, and while most workers agree that the rate of loss of SO_2 depends directly on the concentration of this gas, there is some difference of opinion as to the speed of the process (quantum yields range from ~ 0.3 to two orders of magnitude lower). The lower values are now preferred for atmospheric levels of SO_2[3, 6–12].

The more recent work[12] suggests that the rate of SO_2 photo-oxidation in air is lower than that reported in the earlier studies, the discrepancy perhaps arising from inadequate attention being paid to 'conditioning' of the vessel walls in previous experiments. Wall effects can be a serious problem in gas kinetics since the surface may act as a third body in combination reactions, exaggerating the importance of reactions that would otherwise occur only slowly in the gas interior. Only by altering surface-to-volume ratios, stirring, or better still using a flow system, can such effects be minimised.

Applying results of earlier work, absorption of energy in the spectral region described leads to either the first excited singlet from light near 290 nm (designated for convenience ($^1SO_2$)) or triplet ($^3SO_2$) near 390 nm.[‡] Singlet SO_2, if formed, is likely to be rapidly quenched by collisions with other molecules (since spin restrictions on energy transfer are less limiting) so that chemical reaction is thought to be mainly from the triplet state.

$$SO_2^* + O_2 + M \rightarrow SO_4 + M \tag{4}$$

[†] Quantum yield is defined as the efficiency of a photochemical process, namely the number of moles reacting per Einstein of light absorbed.

[‡] Singlet and triplet excited states differ according to the electron spins and are of different energies. For the meaning of symbols P, D, Π, etc. the reader is referred to a chemistry text.

Presence of a 'third body', M, is a necessary restriction for the combination of atoms and small molecules. It serves to carry away the excess energy that is produced in the formation of a new bond and in the absence of M the energy resides in the molecule which is then likely to break this bond within a period of bond vibration. The reactive intermediate SO_4 is thought to be isolated in the reaction of the oxygen atom with SO_3[13].

Reaction (3) is followed by:

$$SO + O_2 \rightarrow SO_3 \tag{5}$$

$$\text{and} \quad SO_4 + SO_2 \rightarrow 2SO_3. \tag{6}$$

An assessment of the importance of reactions between SO_2 molecules can only be arrived at from a knowledge of the rate constants, atmospheric concentrations and competing reactions. However reactions (3) to (5) gain credence in the sense of their dependence on oxygen concentration[12]. An alternative is:

$$SO_4 + O_2 \rightarrow SO_3 + O_3, \tag{7}$$

which must rely for its validity on the detection of ozone (O_3) in the system.

Sulphur dioxide absorbs more light in the region 320–390 nm when dissolved in liquid water than when it exists as molecules in the gas phase[3]. This may be seen as a perturbing effect of the polar solvent (i.e. water) on the absorption spectrum of SO_2, or else the spectral properties of entities H_2SO_3, HSO_3^- and SO_3^{2-} differ from their parent gas. Hence SO_2 in liquid water droplets† in the atmosphere will take up more energy than the same amount of SO_2 in the gas phase.

Nitrogen oxides

Nitrogen dioxide (NO_2) is of prime importance as a precursor of the many compounds that are the products of photochemical and thermal reactions in the atmospheric mix. It shows broad absorption over the visible and ultraviolet range of the solar spectrum. The bond dissociation energy of NO_2 to produce a normal $NO(^2\pi)$ and $O(^3P)$ is 300 kJ mol^{-1} or the energy of the quantum at 394 nm:

$$NO_2 + h\nu \rightarrow NO(^2\pi) + O(^3P). \tag{8}$$

This suggests that photodissociation is only possible at < 394 nm, but some

---

† A dispersion of particulates in air is known as an aerosol – dust and smokes if solids, fogs and mists if liquid, in loose terms. The distinction within the two broad categories of solid and liquid aerosols depends more on size than chemical nature.

still occurs at 400 nm, or somewhat above, due to the availability of the internal energy of the NO_2 molecule to augment absorbed energy. However while NO_2 does absorb above about 435 nm and fluorescence has been observed in laboratory experiments, little chemical change takes place in pure NO_2 or NO_2/O_2 mixtures. In more complex mixed systems with, for example, hydrocarbons, the situation may be quite different. Nitrogen dioxide is known also to form the double molecule nitrogen tetroxide (N_2O_4), pressure-dependent association that produces most N_2O_4 in the liquid phase of NO_2 and hence in our systems is only significant at higher pressures of NO_2. From the known equilibrium constant, K, for the association and the absorption coefficient of N_2O_4, the rate of energy absorption by N_2O_4 by comparison with NO_2 seems quite small.

In irradiated NO_2/air systems the principal processes suggested, besides (8), are:

$$O + O_2 + M \rightarrow O_3 + M \qquad k = 10^8 \ M^{-2} \ s^{-1} \qquad (9)$$

$$E_a = 4 \ kJ \ mol^{-1}$$

$$(\Delta H = -492 \ kJ \ mol^{-1})$$

$$O + NO_2 + M \rightarrow NO_3 + M \quad k = 10^{11} \ M^{-2} \ s^{-1} \qquad (10)$$

$$(E_a \sim 0)$$

$$\Delta H = -207 \ kJ \ mol^{-1}$$

$$O_3 + NO_2 \rightarrow NO_3 + O_2 \qquad k = 2 \times 10^4 \ M^{-1} \ s^{-1} \qquad (11)$$

$$E_a = 20 \ kJ \ mol^{-1}$$

$$\Delta H = 105 \ kJ \ mol^{-1}$$

$$O + NO_2 \rightarrow NO + O_2 \qquad k = 5 \times 10^9 \ M^{-1} \ s^{-1} \qquad (12)$$

$$E_a = 0$$

$$\Delta H = -190 \ kJ \ mol^{-1}$$

$$O + NO + M \rightarrow NO_2 + M \qquad k = 10^{10} \ M^{-2} \ s^{-1} \qquad (13)$$

$$(E_a \sim 0)$$

$$\Delta H = -301 \ kJ \ mol^{-1}.$$

On the basis of (8) and (9), O_3 and NO would be formed in comparable amounts, and since the destruction of O_3 and regeneration of NO_2 would rely on the encounter of an NO and O_3 molecule:

$$O_3 + NO \rightarrow O_2 + NO_2 \qquad k = 1 \times 10^7 \ \text{M}^{-1} \ \text{s}^{-1} \qquad (14)$$

$$E_a = 5 \ \text{kJ mol}^{-1}$$

$$\Delta H = -200 \ \text{kJ mol}^{-1}$$

the relative proportions of NO and O_3 should be maintained. The fact that O_3 yields in such systems tend to decline relative to NO is the rationale for (11).

On structural grounds the argument for the existence of the entity NO_3 is persuasive[3], either being a symmetrical nitrate

It has been invoked to explain the relatively short life or residence time of carbon monoxide (CO) in the atmosphere. The thermal (i.e. ambient temperature) oxidation of CO by molecular oxygen (O_2) is relatively slow and is only slightly faster by O_3[14] (for the latter the rate constant, k, at 300 K is $< 10^6 \ \text{M}^{-1} \ \text{s}^{-1}$), but the oxidation could be achieved by the reaction

$$NO_3 + CO \rightarrow NO_2 + CO_2. \qquad (15)$$

(NO_2 in the oxidation $CO + NO_2 \rightarrow CO_2 + NO$ is thought not to be important.) Situations where O_3 accumulates will be discussed later in the context of mixed systems.

The existence of nitric acid (HNO_3) in the upper atmosphere may result from the reaction of hydroxyl radicals (OH)[15], the single dot representing an unpaired electron,

$$\cdot OH + NO_2 + M \rightarrow HNO_3 + M, \qquad (16)$$

or in the lower atmosphere from gaseous nitrogen pentoxide (N_2O_5; equivalent to an adduct or addition compound of NO_2 and NO_3) reacting with water perhaps from aerosol droplets

$$N_2O_5 + H_2O \rightarrow 2HNO_3. \qquad (17)$$

The reaction:

$$3NO_2 + H_2O = 2HNO_3 + NO, \qquad (18)$$

written as a stoichiometric or overall equation of uncertain mechanism, requiring high local concentrations of NO_2, may convert up to 10% of NO_2 to HNO_3 in moist air at ambient temperatures. Whatever its origin HNO_3 is known to absorb near 320 nm extending to shorter wavelengths while

N_2O_5 has a longer wavelength cut-off, near 380 nm. The primary process during the irradiation of HNO_3 is:

$$HNO_3 + h\nu \rightarrow \cdot OH + NO_2 \qquad (19)$$

(i.e. the reverse of (16)), putting OH into the system[15].

There is much that is still speculative in this area but $O(^3P)$ at least is thought to react very slowly with HNO_3 vapour[16]. On the other hand a possible but so far unproved fragmentation of HNO_3 is to give hydrogen atoms and NO_3. If hydrogen atoms from this or another source exist, the hydroperoxyl radical (HO_2) formed by rapid addition of O_2 to H, is bound to be involved. This again is a well-known intermediate in systems under ionising radiation and two of its many reactions are the production of nitrous acid (HNO_2) from NO_2:

$$HO_2 + NO_2 \rightarrow HNO_2 + O_2 \qquad (20)$$

and the reaction of HO_2 and NO to produce NO_2 and OH radicals, rapid even at 300 K. It is clear that there is still much to be done in the unambiguous identification of intermediates in atmospheric chemistry.

Nitrous oxide (N_2O) is another oxide of nitrogen in the lower atmosphere (level ~ 0.5 ppm). The man-made contribution is relatively small, the bulk coming from natural sources. It is relatively inert. Reactions with $O(^1D)$ and (11) and (14) are discussed elsewhere[16]. The photodissociation reaction to give N_2 and an oxygen atom occurs at wavelengths shorter than the visible.

Ammonia

Ammonia (NH_3) does not absorb light in the region 800–290 nm and its chemical fate is probably determined by reactions with acids or acid-forming oxides and possibly through reactions with radical intermediates. These will be discussed later.

Hydrogen sulphide

Hydrogen sulphide (H_2S) has both technological and natural origins, and is removed by non-photochemical processes. The H–S bond strength is ~ 340 kJ mol^{-1}, corresponding to ~ 350 nm, but H_2S does not absorb above 250 nm. Droplet-phase reactions of H_2S need further examination. It is possible that it reacts fairly rapidly with oxygen atoms ($k = 2 \times 10^7$ M^{-1} s^{-1}).

Oxygen

Oxygen (O_2) absorbs very weakly at the red end of the spectrum but involvement in atmospheric chemistry of the slightly excited molecules so formed is still conjectural.

Water

Fragmentation to produce either $H + OH$ or $H_2 + O$ requires about 490 kJ mol^{-1} but water only absorbs at wavelengths shorter than 200 nm.

Hydrocarbons

Carbon compounds both saturated and unsaturated (i.e. containing double bonds) of low molecular weight are transparent in the range 290–800 nm, that is they are not primary absorbers. Interest in them stems from their reactivity with other substances present initially, or produced in thermal or photochemical processes (e.g. oxidation of olefins by O_3 or oxygen atoms to produce carbonyl compounds–aldehydes and ketones). There is, however, some interest in aromatic hydrocarbons (benzene-like derivatives) as sensitisers for singlet O_2 formation. It is suggested, for instance, that due to the interaction with O_2, the absorption spectrum of an aromatic hydrocarbon is shifted to longer wavelengths (important for atmospheric photochemistry) resulting in organic hyperoxide formation.

There is recent interest in polycyclic aromatic hydrocarbons (PAHs) produced in combusting systems under conditions of limited oxygen access. The carcinogenic threat they pose is well-known but little is known of their reactions with other substances in the air.

Products

In laboratory studies the period of the experiment can be controlled so that the likelihood of products themselves becoming reactants for other processes can be minimised by keeping conversions low ($< 5\%$). The natural environment recognises no such restriction and O_3 can, for example, become a primary reactant:

$$O_3 + h\nu \rightarrow O_2 + O(^3P). \tag{21}$$

The energy required for this split (103 kJ mol^{-1}) is somewhat beyond the long wavelength end of the visible spectrum so the process is easily facilitated by sunlight. The normal O_3 molecule is probably a singlet and the very strong absorption in the ultraviolet (> 2000 times stronger than in the visible region of the spectrum) suggests that the visible absorption (peaking near 600 nm with a long wavelength tail near 800 nm) is a 'forbidden' one from spin correlation rules, with the excited state O_3^* from which O_2 and O are formed, being itself a triplet state.

The process

$$O(^3P) + H_2O \rightarrow 2OH \tag{22}$$

$$\Delta H = +75 \text{ kJ mol}^{-1}$$

is not likely to be very significant because of its endothermic nature. However the energetic $O(^1D)$, with 190 kJ mol^{-1} more energy than $O(^3P)$† and probably the dominant fragment in the ultraviolet photolysis of O_3, produces OH radicals from water with ease[17], [18], [19]. In the absence of reacting substances,

$$O_3 + h\nu \rightarrow O_2 + O \tag{23}$$

followed by

$$O + O_3 \rightarrow 2O_2 \tag{24}$$

explains the quantum yield of 2 frequently observed for O_3 destruction. It is worth noting that some tropospheric O_3 is man-made but there is a substantial contribution by downward drift from the stratosphere.

Sulphur trioxide may be a primary absorber near the short wave-length limit:

$$SO_3 + h\nu \rightarrow SO_2 + O(^3P) \tag{25}$$

requiring 347 kJ mol^{-1} (346 nm), i.e. the reverse of (29). Another possibility is

$$SO_3 + h\nu \rightarrow SO + O_2 \tag{26}$$

requiring 397 kJ mol^{-1} (300 nm). Neither is likely to be important unless SO_3 builds up to high concentrations in the unlikely event of other reactive compounds or sinks being absent, or of reactions such as:

$$O(^3P) + SO_3 \rightarrow SO_2 + O_2 \tag{27}$$

$$k = 3 \times 10^4 \text{ M}^{-1} \text{s}^{-1}$$

$$E_a = 4 \text{ kJ mol}^{-1}$$

$$\Delta H = -13 \text{ kJ mol}^{-1}.$$

not intervening[12]. The photochemistry of carbonyl compounds formed from hydrocarbon oxidation is well-known, the cleavage in acetone, for example, being fairly typical:

$$CH_3COCH_3 + h\nu \rightarrow CH_3\dot{C}O + \cdot CH_3. \tag{28}$$

The acetyl (CH_3CO) and methyl (CH_3) radicals take part in further processes that lead to the formation of peroxyacetyl nitrate, mentioned later. These again are light-sensitive, leading to a further degree of complexity.

† $O(^1D)$ denotes the singlet, and $O(^3P)$ the triplet state.

Interactions

Where possible the discussion so far has been confined to one substance at a time, but inevitably since oxygen is an ever-present, reactive and abundant component of the atmosphere, this has involved consideration of the reactions that the substance experiences with oxygen and its products. In this sense simpler interactions have been examined. Some attention has been given to NO/NO_2, NO/O_3 and NO_2/O_3 systems. The processes

$$O + SO_2 + M \rightarrow SO_3 + M \quad k = 3 \times 10^{10} \, M^{-2} \, s^{-1} \tag{29}$$

and

$$O_3 + SO_2 \rightarrow SO_3 + O_2 \quad k = \, <10^{-1} \, M^{-1} \, s^{-1} \tag{30}$$

$$E_a = \, \sim 40 \, kJ \, mol^{-1}$$

need further study. Little has been said of thermal interactions of SO_2/NO_2, O_3/SO_2, NO/SO_2, although in the last-mentioned system it is suggested that in photochemical conditions NO would have a retarding effect[7] on SO_2 oxidation due to reaction (31) below, where otherwise 2 molecules of SO_3 might be produced from (6):

$$SO_4 + NO \rightarrow SO_3 + NO_2. \tag{31}$$

The suggestion is just plausible. The NH_3/NO_2 reaction (producing N_2, N_2O, NO and H_2O) has been followed above 600 K[20]. A long extrapolation to temperatures relevant here makes $k = 1 \times 10^{-10} \, M^{-1} \, s^{-1}$, quite small, but an interesting feature is the production of an amine radical (NH_2) in the first step:

$$NH_3 + NO_2 \rightarrow \cdot NH_2 + HNO_2 \tag{32}$$

$$E_a = 116 \, kJ \, mol^{-1}$$

$$\Delta H = 103 \, kJ \, mol^{-1}.$$

As seen the rate is quite negligible, however.

Interest in the NH_3/SO_2 mixture stems from the reactions of these compounds in the liquid phase with reference then to atmospheric droplets. As far as the writer is aware not much is known of their reactions in thermal or photochemical conditions in the gas phase.

It is inescapable that hydrocarbons add a further, much complicating dimension to the subject of atmospheric interactions, made more difficult by the necessity to consider solid particulates, aerosol droplets etc. in the

mix. Paraffinic or saturated hydrocarbons (RH) are probably less complicated to understand than olefins.

The insertion of excited SO_2 to produce sulphinic acids[5]:

$$RH + SO_2{}^* \rightarrow RSO_2H, \tag{33}$$

goes easily with short wave-length radiation but the question of its importance
in atmospheric photochemistry is still open. The O_3 reaction with paraffins
is held to be fairly slow. On the other hand hydrogen atom abstraction by
oxygen to form hydroxyl radicals is well substantiated for $O(^1D)$ but less
certain for $O(^3P)$[21, 22, 23]:

$$O(^1D) + RH \rightarrow \cdot OH + \cdot R \tag{34}$$

$$\text{Methane } k = 1 \times 10^{11} \, \text{M}^{-1} \, \text{s}^{-1}.$$

The importance of this process is that hydroxyl (OH) and alkyl (R) radicals
are now present in the system.

By contrast the ground state oxygen atom addition to the double bond of
an olefin has been well-studied[24, 25, 26]:

$$\underset{\text{ethylene}}{O(^3P) + C_2H_4} \rightarrow \cdot CH_3 + \cdot CHO \tag{35}$$

$$\text{for ethylene} \begin{cases} k = 5 \times 10^8 \, \text{M}^{-1} \, \text{s}^{-1} \\ E_a = 5 \, \text{kJ mol}^{-1} \end{cases}$$

$$\text{for but-1-ene} \begin{cases} k = 1 \times 10^{10} \, \text{M}^{-1} \, \text{s}^{-1} \\ E_a = 3 \, \text{kJ mol}^{-1} \end{cases}$$

From the relative reactivities of various olefins the oxygen atom emerges as
being electron-seeking or electrophilic. The process is relatively fast although
spin-forbidden. This has led to a study of possible correlations between
activation energies and excitation to the triplet state of the olefin[26], i.e.
the reaction may follow from excitation to the triplet state of the olefin on
approach of the $O(^3P)$ atom. The short-lived biradical may then fragment
or rearrange, written schematically as:

(using the convention of dots for electrons involved and single and double
strokes for single and double bonds. A single dot then signifies an unpaired
electron, i.e. reactive free radical).

An early suggestion that conjugated dienes (double bonds in proximity allowing Π orbital overlap) promote the oxidation of NO to NO_2 was followed up[27].

The *thermal* reaction does occur but is seven to twenty-five times slower (depending on the hydrocarbon) than the diene-promoted photo-oxidation of NO. The reaction is autocatalytic in the sense that NO_2 itself acts as a catalyst, the suggested first step in the process being the addition of a molecule of NO_2 to a molecule of the di-olefin.

Some broad correlations are possible[28]: olefins with double bonds near the interior of the molecule are more reactive than olefins with terminal double bonds, and substitution by groups other than H on double bonds increases reactivity for both aliphatic and aromatic compounds; cyclo-olefins are more reactive than straight-chain compounds and the amount of strain in ring compounds is also relevant. There is some overlap of course between these categories of reactivity, but in general it may be said that the NO_2 molecule acts like an electron-seeking reagent and features of the hydrocarbon molecule that promote electron release enhance reactivity. The importance of NO_2 of course relates, in the photochemical case to the onset of O_3 and aerosol formation, though in its own right under thermal conditions NO_2 is more damaging than NO. The initial step for ethylene is as follows[29]:

$$NO_2 + C_2H_4 \rightarrow products \tag{36}$$

$$k = 2 \times 10^{-3} \, M^{-1} \, s^{-1}$$

The corresponding process for di-olefins must be considerably more rapid to be significant in the atmospheric environment. Figures such as $76 \, M^{-1} \, s^{-1}$ or $1.9 \times 10^{-4} \, ppm^{-1} \, min^{-1}$ appear in the literature.

By the addition of compounds such as benzaldehyde which are known to be good free-radical traps, the inhibition of NO_2 formation from NO in the presence of hydrocarbons has been demonstrated in laboratory experiments[30]. How realistic this is as a possible way of controlling pollution by the deliberate injection of foreign material into the atmosphere must remain speculative.

Addition of molecular oxygen to hydrocarbon fragments to form peroxy radicals is important in the formation of O_3 and organic nitrates[31, 32]. This may be summarised by alkyl radicals from (34) but more abundantly from the light-induced fragmentation of carbonyl compounds shown in (28):

$$R \cdot + O_2 \rightarrow RO_2^{\cdot} \tag{37}$$

and

$$RCO \cdot + O_2 \rightarrow R(CO)O_2^{\cdot}, \tag{38}$$

both reactions requiring a third body, followed by:

$$R(CO)O_2^2 + O_2 \rightarrow R(CO)O \cdot + O_3 \tag{39}$$

$$R(CO)O \cdot + NO_2 \rightarrow R(CO)O\,NO_2 \tag{40}$$

and

$$R(CO)O_2^2 + NO_2 \rightarrow R(CO)O_2\,NO_2, \tag{41}$$

which is peroxyacetyl nitrate (PAN) if $R = CH_3$. (This is not an exhaustive list of possible processes.)

The generation of peroxyacylnitrates (the general term for $R(CO)O_2\,NO_2$) in thermal (low-temperature, dark) reactions from acetaldehyde (CH_3CHO), O_2 and N_2O_5 may suggest that NO_3 is involved[32], and O_3 is not the important precursor it was thought to be. On the topic of oxidation of unsaturated hydrocarbons the influence of NO is relevant and of practical significance. Olefin (and aromatic) oxidation under light increases with increasing NO concentration (up to $\simeq 0.5$ ppm NO) and thereafter decreases, but depending on the nature and concentration of the hydrocarbon[33, 34]. Olefin oxidation may be initiated by oxidation of some NO to NO_2, the further autocatalytic oxidation of NO in the presence of NO_2 and hydrocarbon as discussed above, and the formation of O_3 from the photobreakdown of NO_2, i.e.

$$NO_2 + h\nu \rightarrow NO + O, \tag{42}$$

followed by

$$O + O_2 + M \rightarrow O_3 + M \tag{43}$$

and direct O_3 addition, or simply reaction (35). Inhibition by NO could be associated with reaction (14), in which case inhibition really means prolonging the onset of oxidising species (O or O_3) able to react with the hydrocarbon. This exemplifies the dynamic nature of chemical systems for which the interpretative argument becomes forceful only when rate constants and appropriate concentrations are applied, to demonstrate that competition is effective in the experimentally observed regions. To obtain the relevant information, sources outside the atmospheric chemistry and air pollution context frequently have to be culled[35, 36].

From this discussion of thermal and photochemical reactions in hydrocarbon/SO_2 and hydrocarbon/NO_x systems, mixtures which have more primary components and hence are possibly more realistic, should be considered.

The purpose of one of the earliest studies of the SO_2 system[6] was to follow the rate of photochemical oxidation at low concentrations of SO_2 in air, and in the presence of sufficient water vapour to permit aerosol formation. The process was found to be first-order with respect to SO_2 and there was a linear increase in H_2SO_4 aerosol with time for a given SO_2 concentration, with the percentage conversion in equal intervals of time roughly constant and unaffected by changes in humidity in the range studied. The suggested rate-determining step is reaction (4). While there is little in subsequent work to refute this, the matter of oxygen dependence is still open.

In this study NO_2 gas and sodium chloride aerosol added to the air stream in separate experiments had no measurable effect on the rate of oxidation, which was also negligible in the dark. Ozone also, produced by the photolysis of NO_2 (reactions (8) and (9)) is not significant in producing SO_3 at these concentrations (reaction (30)). However, the effect of some reducible metal salts in dispersed droplets was marked, Mn^{2+}, Ni^{2+}, each significantly increased the rate of SO_2 oxidation, in the dark and under irradiation. From the relatively slow rate of photo-oxidation in the absence of such aerosols, and the observed rapid decrease in visibility in polluted atmospheres, the authors conclude that such liquid phase reactions may be substantially more effective.

This was pursued later[37] by the same school to the expected conclusion that the rate of formation of H_2SO_4 in aerosol droplets depends on the partial pressure of SO_2 in the external atmosphere and the nature and concentration of catalytic substances present in the droplet phase. For a high concentration of catalyst, reaction takes place in the outer shell of the drop so that SO_2 is oxidised before diffusing into the interior. The catalytic reaction may take place, of course, in the dark as well as under light. A subtle distinction, however, may exist between droplets formed by photochemical oxidation of SO_2 in the gas phase and subsequent hydration, and those where SO_2 enters the droplet and is subsequently oxidised catalytically. If the droplet is not in vapour equilibrium with its surroundings it will, on entering an area of, say, lower relative humidity, begin to evaporate, but the higher concentration of H_2SO_4, by reducing the vapour pressure of the drop, will slow down the evaporation rate. Droplets formed by the catalytic process may then be somewhat larger than those formed photochemically, there being a distribution about the mean size in each case. It still remains to be shown how prevalent such catalysts are in polluted air.

The catalytic droplet system was examined recently in some detail[38]. With some criticism of earlier methods of aerosol stabilisation, these authors propose a new technique of depositing aerosol particles on an inert substrate such as polytetrafluoroethylene (PTFE) and under the conditions specified higher rates of SO_2 oxidation are associated with higher humidities. Since aerosol particles hydrate to solution drops at higher relative humidities, the predominant mass transfer mechanism is absorption of SO_2 by the catalyst drops, followed by chemical reaction in the liquid phase. This can be seen mechanistically as a composite of chemical and physical processes:

Physical

SO_2 (gas) → SO_2 (surface) i.e. gas phase diffusion

SO_2 (surface → SO_2 (droplet interface) i.e. interfacial transfer

SO_2 (interface) → SO_2 (bulk solution) i.e. liquid phase diffusion.

Chemical (several steps)

SO_2 (solution) → oxidation, hydration.

Results indicate that the overall rate is controlled by the chemical reaction; In agreement with other data, it was found that Mn II salts are very effective as catalysts and NaCl least effective[6]. Cupric chloride ($CuCl_2$) entered into a net chemical reaction with dissolved SO_2

$$SO_2 + 2CuCl_2 + 2H_2O = 2CuCl + H_2SO_4 + 2HCl \tag{44}$$
$$\text{(overall stoichiometric reaction)}$$

so while it may not qualify for consideration as a catalyst, it does as a reacting substance. The first-order dependence on SO_2 concentration is confirmed and emphasises the importance of metal compounds both dissolved in fog droplets (where they may have in fact acted as condensation nuclei) in humid climates, and possibly as particulates in drier regions.

The initial rapid conversion of SO_2 is ascribed to the initial rapid solution of gas phase SO_2 into the catalyst solution drop:

$$K_1 = 10^{-2}$$
$$SO_2 + H_2O \rightleftharpoons H_2SO_3, + H_2O \rightleftharpoons H_3O^+ + HSO_3{}^-$$
$$\Updownarrow K_2 = 10^{-7}$$
$$H_3O^+ + SO_3{}^{2-} \tag{45}$$

on further dissociation.

Equilibrium or acid dissociation constants K_1 and K_2 are for the dissociations of the first and second protons of sulphurous acid (H_2SO_3). The initial rate of reaction then is slower than the rate of absorption, the diffusion of ions $HSO_3{}^-$ and $SO_3{}^{2-}$ contributing to the total diffusion of SO_2. This initial stage of rapid solution and conversion subsequently comes under the influence of the increase in H_2SO_4 concentration in the droplet, and its dissociation:

$$K_1 \text{ (large)}$$
$$H_2O + SO_3 \rightleftharpoons H_2SO_4, + H_2O \rightleftharpoons H_3O^+ + HSO_4^-$$

$$\Updownarrow K_2 = 10^{-2}$$

$$H_3O^+ + SO_4^{2-} \tag{46}$$

An observation from many sources is that SO_2 oxidation in the liquid phase is retarded by acid, due probably to the suppression of dissociation in (45), since HSO_3^- reacts only slowly and H_2SO_3 barely at all. In the steady state situation then, as one molecule of SO_2 is oxidised in the catalyst droplet, it will rapidly be replaced by entry of another SO_2 molecule from the gas phase to maintain the saturation solubility.

It has been proposed that in the oxidation of sulphurous acid (H_2SO_3 or $H_2O \cdot SO_2$) in catalyst solutions, the reactive intermediate is a metal sulphite complex that picks up an O_2 molecule and reacts[39]. In this case and in conformity with the effect of acid, one has to consider the dissociation shown in (45) (K_2 for instance being 10^{-7} at 300 K) and whether complex formation promotes the dissociation. Intuition suggests that no very great discrepancy would be expected between metal sulphite oxidation and HSO_3^- oxidation since in many processes the proton (H^+) mimics the effect of metal ions in complex formation. Oxidation may, however, be a special case since O_2 binding capacity demonstrated by metal ions may not be easily reproduced by H^+.

With respect to the water vapour content it was found that oxidation proceeds at all humidities but is much slower at low humidities. In the dry state oxidation may not proceed at all by the mechanism given and other pathways are found. In this respect the effect of dusts, e.g. of metal oxide, is a subject that has barely begun to be explored. On the other hand the subject of reactions in droplets is a highly relevant one and the importance of such factors as the ionic strength of the medium in reactions between ions, deactivation of excited molecules and atoms in photochemical reactions, radical–radical recombination due to the operation of the 'cage' effect usually observed in solution processes, together with the unique influence of surface curvature, have yet to be assessed.

Condensation nuclei in the atmosphere range down in size to about $0.1 \, \mu m$ (~ 100 molecular diameters) while rain drops may go up to five orders of magnitude greater. Aerosol droplets are about midway in this range. Condensation as a whole is an exothermic process but it is a well-known physical fact that it requires energy to create a surface, an expression of which is the surface tension or interfacial tension between a liquid and a gas. This interfacial discontinuity may be at least partially relieved by the adherence of electric charge to the surface. As a result aerosols like rain drops are expected to become electrically charged when an increase in surface occurs. Correspondingly condensation – evaporation cycles will produce a growth in concentration of dissolved substances leading to supersaturation, one cause of which could be energy required for the creation of a new surface, and in this case a solid surface within the aerosol droplet.

These are still unanswered questions, and the statement that it is immaterial whether the aqueous phase is dispersed as droplets or present as bulk liquid allowing the direct application of bulk liquid phase phenomena[40], must be viewed with some caution. In fact it may not be too speculative to predict that at the high supersaturations that appear possible in aerosol systems of NaCl and H_2SO_4, some release of hydrochloric acid (HCl) into the gas phase may take place.

Laboratory and field studies[41] substantiate that NH_3 increases the rate of oxidation of SO_2 in conditions of high humidity. Sulphur dioxide oxidation has been recently reviewed[40] to the conclusion, briefly discussed before, that the oxidation is pH-dependent and NH_3 serves to maintain a favourably high pH. A feature is that for a given initial concentration of SO_2 the reaction slows down with time, as might be expected for depletion of the reactant. Of more interest is that the temperature coefficient is 'negative', that is, the over-all rate of reaction decreases with increasing temperature. The explanation is that the increasing solubility of SO_2 and NH_3 in water droplets at the lower temperatures more than counterbalances the fall in the rate of sulphite oxidation.

As far as human health is concerned it is probably true to say that am-monium sulphate particulates are preferable to sulphuric acid (but aestheti-cally displeasing due to the obscuration of light). The same may hold for vegetation damage, corrosion etc.

Sulphur dioxide/hydrocarbon/nitrogen oxides systems have attracted attention for their very real bearing on the atmospheric problem. It is suggested[7] that NO_2 enhances the oxidation of SO_2 through reaction (8) providing $O(^3P)$ atoms for reaction (29) or for O_3 formation through (43) followed by (30). As mentioned previously, NO has a suppressive effect (see reaction (31)), but the situation is complex since NO_2 is produced. For a number of olefins at low concentrations, considerable enhancement of light scattering is observed in the presence of water vapour. As much light scatter-ing can be produced at lower concentrations of hydrocarbons as at higher ones if the residence time in flow systems is longer – probably corresponding to longer contact times in the atmospheric situation. Further, the greater the SO_2 level, the greater the light scattering; it must be borne in mind, however, that this may be due to either a few large (possibly asymmetric) particles or many small particles.

In general the presence of SO_2 is required for significant aerosol formation, but it is worth noting that cyclohexene was one of the few olefins that produced substantial aerosol in the absence of SO_2. This is interesting in connection with reported hazes in forested areas thought to be due to the release of terpenes from vegetation and their subsequent photoxidation[42].

From the above study it was concluded that small amounts of SO_2 in the presence of hydrocarbons can provide sufficient acidic nuclei for condensation and chemical reaction of other materials. The nature of the aerosol formed has been a component of several studies[43] and nothing found has been in basic conflict with conclusions discussed above. For instance H_2SO_4 was the major constituent and the amount of carbon-containing material was small, at high humidities. At low humidities in addition to H_2SO_4, (inorganic) nitrogen compounds were detected. However, mass balances in many of the reported studies are seldom satisfactory.

A later investigation along similar lines[44] ($SO_2 - NO_x - 1$ butane, H_2O) reiterates the importance of the role of H_2O vapour. In dry air, however, there was no little apparent loss of SO_2 with or without illumination. At greater than 30% relative humidity (28 °C), SO_2 concentration falls on illumination. For this system, illumination causes decreases in SO_2, NO and olefin concentrations while NO_2 increases. Later in the experiment O_3, acetaldehyde (CH_3CHO) and propionaldehyde (CH_3CH_2CHO) and aerosol appear. Nitrogen dioxide and O_3 reach peak concentrations and then begin to decrease. The picture looks remarkably like a smog profile with the difference that in the latter both emissions and light intensity alter through the day.

Some conclusions emerge; for example, O_3, aerosols and peroxyacetyl nitrate do not begin to form until the NO_2 concentration has increased appreciably. As discussed earlier, formation of such substances depends on the provision of oxygen atoms, probably from a primary photochemical process. Addition of H_2O vapour decreases the time it takes to reach the NO_2 maximum (or perhaps increases the overall rate NO → NO_2). Water vapour also decreases the time to reach the O_3 maximum but here the maximum is lower than in the absence of H_2O. At lower humidities the effect of SO_2 is to increase the time taken to reach the maximum O_3 concentration and to raise this maximum. It is thought that O_3 can build up to higher concentrations because the reactions that remove O_3 are slowed down more than those that form it (or else an entirely new reaction intervenes). At higher ($>65\%$) relative humidity the opposite effect is again observed in that the time to reach the maximum O_3 concentration is considerably shortened with increasing SO_2 and the maximum O_3 is itself decreased.

More recently, mixed systems have been studied in a logical sequence[46] to unravel factors important in aerosol formation. The reactants were SO_2, an olefinic hydrocarbon and O_3 – a situation much simplified by using the photochemically produced oxidant (O_3), but without the complication that SO_2 in the mixture is also irradiated. In the absence of the olefin, cis-pent-2-ene, O_3 and SO_2 concentrations fall only slowly on mixing, and only a slow increase in the sulphur-containing aerosol is noticed. When olefin is injected a rapid increase in aerosol formation takes place. Since olefins do not react rapidly with SO_2, it is proposed that a product of the ozone–olefin reaction reacts with SO_2 (e.g. for O_3/hex-1-ene reaction, $k = 7 \times 10^3 \, M^{-1} \, s^{-1}$).

Aerosol formation is first-order with respect to O_3 and olefin, and since SO_2 has no effect on the rate of reaction of olefin, it is presumed that O_3 removal is also unaffected by the presence of SO_2. This is confirmed by chemiluminescence measurements; further, olefin and O_3 react together in a $1:1$ stoichiometry both in the presence and absence of SO_2, but SO_2 did give increased product yields (e.g. acetaldehyde, propionaldehyde). Similar results were observed for other olefins.

The oxidation of SO_2 to form an H_2SO_4 aerosol is usually observed in the presence of a reacting mixture of O_3 and olefin. As there is no induction period, oxidation commences immediately on the addition of olefin and ceases when all O_3 has reacted. Results support the earlier conclusion that olefins with double bonds near the interior of the molecule are more reactive than olefins with double bonds near the ends. Early work by others also suggested that the formation of ozonides (O_3 addition products) of olefins decreases with increasing carbon number, explaining the lack of effect of higher olefins such as decene and tetradecene.

This study enables aerosol formation to be summarised thus:

$$O_3 + \text{olefin} \rightarrow \text{reactive intermediate (possibly an internal ion)} \qquad (47)$$

$$\text{Reactive intermediate} + SO_2 \rightarrow \text{oxidised product forming aerosol} \qquad (48)$$

the first being the rate-determining step. Similar results were obtained when air was replaced by N_2 so that O_2 was not involved. The nature of the aerosol was roughly confirmed when it was dissolved from a membrane filter and gave a positive reaction for sulphate. This is an area for further work since identification of organic constituents would be useful. A somewhat provoking observation is that the aerosol formation rate (relative to O_3 reaction rate) decreased with increasing relative humidity at all SO_2 concentrations. Also the presence of iron oxide particles had no effect. This is in contrast to the conclusions of other investigations that powdered oxides of aluminium, chromium, calcium, iron, lead and vanadium increase the rate of oxidation of SO_2 in air without sunlight[9]. Reactions on the surfaces of solid particulates are clearly an area for further study.

Concluding remarks

The finer details of droplet phase reactions[47] need examining. Oxidation reactions by ozone (O_3) in synthetic fogs[48] and in bulk aqueous systems by the rapid response stopped-flow technique[49] indicate that droplet phase reactions contribute significantly to overall changes in the atmospheric environment. While major end-products of atmospheric processes are largely known, minor products and reactive intermediates remain to be identified. Such products may be minor in terms of amount formed but could be quite important with respect to effects on vegetation, material deterioration etc. $O(^3P)$ is commonly held to be the main oxygen atom species in the atmosphere. Provided there is absorption of radiation at the short wave-length end of the visible spectrum, the quantum is more than sufficient for the production of $O(^1D)$. If this is so, many new reactions will intervene, not the least of which would be the production of hydroxyl radicals (OH) from water. Also the reaction:

$$O(^1D) + NH_3 \rightarrow \cdot NH_2 + \cdot OH$$

is near to being thermoneutral and a rate constant has been determined ($k = \sim 1 \times 10^6 \, M^{-1} \, s^{-1}$)[50]. If this proceeds with reasonable facility the amine radical (NH_2) will undergo subsequent reactions such as insertion into carbon–carbon double bonds, leading ultimately to organic amines. Hydroxyl radicals from a number of sources are considered of increasing importance in atmospheric chemistry and may account for the relatively short life of carbon monoxide (CO) in the atmosphere:

$$\cdot OH + CO \rightarrow CO_2 + \cdot H \qquad k = 10^7 \, M^{-1} \, s^{-1} \qquad (49)$$

$$E_a = 0.5 \, kJ \, mol^{-1}$$

followed by production of the hydroperoxy radical (HO_2) from the reaction of the hydrogen atom with oxygen. Also the reaction with ammonia (NH_3) goes with some ease:

$$\cdot OH + NH_3 \rightarrow \cdot NH_2 + H_2O \qquad k = 10^8 \, M^{-1} s^{-1} \qquad (50)$$

and similar hydrogen abstraction reactions of low activation energy for a range of hydrocarbons. A summary of important reactions appears elsewhere[51].

No mention has been made of lead halides from lead alkyl combustion in auto fuel, nor of polycyclic aromatic hydrocarbons (PAHs) from combustion under conditions of limited oxygen access. Hydroxyl radical reactions with aromatic molecules have been extensively studied within the framework of reactions initiated by water (both in the liquid and gas phases) under ionising radiation and the rate data can be applied in the atmospheric context. The carcinogenic hazard of PAHs is well recognised and the reactions they experience may in the long-run prove beneficial in terms of human health, since this could lead to short residence times in the atmosphere.

Physico-chemical factors in the first stage of the interaction of air pollutants and their products with vegetation, soils, water and building surfaces warrant some attention.

While impairment of the biochemical and physiological function of plants must be central to the topic of the effects of air pollutants on vegetation, one should be aware of the cleansing potential of vegetative cover. Studies of the relationship of air pollutants to soils are in their infancy but some information is available. For instance the presence of nitric oxide (NO) and water vapour together enhance the sorption of both substances by calcareous soils with the nitrogen compound reducing the basicity of the soil, and being recoverable as nitrate[52]. Parallel studies of porosity, adsorptive area and chemical constitution of soils together with kinetic and mechanistic investigations would be valuable in such research.

Transfer of a gas across a phase boundary, be it during uptake by plant leaves, soils or a water body, to a first approximation has certain simplifying features that may be regarded as being general to all such sink mechanisms:

$$X \, (air) \underset{k_2}{\overset{k_1}{\rightleftharpoons}} X \, (leaf, \, water \, droplet, \, surface \, etc.),$$

where X represents any pollutant gas. In general terms a kinetic procedure for initial transfer gives:

$$speed \; of \; transfer \; v = k_1 A(X)_1,$$

$$1 \rightarrow 2$$

where A is the area of interface, $(X)_1$ the concentration or partial pressure of pollutant gas in the air phase and k_1 a transfer constant analogous to a chemical rate constant, i.e. here a physical rate constant.

If subsequent processes, such as translocation to a leaf interior, chemical reactions that change the nature of the substance etc., are slow then as the concentration in the absorbing phase builds up the reverse process will become noticeable and the net speed of absorption will be the difference in the two rates:

$$v_{net} = v_{1 \to 2} - v_{2 \to 1}.$$

Ultimately, of course, equilibrium will be reached when the two rates are equal. In a real situation this is unlikely to occur to any great extent except perhaps in air/droplet reactions. Sink mechanisms will operate to make the flow predominantly one way, with the rate-limiting step usually diffusion across a laminar unstirred, or still layer. Turbulence in the air phase will reduce the width of this stagnant layer and speed up transfer but never completely eliminate the still layer[53]. All such may be seen as applications of expressions for diffusion phenomena under a concentration gradient.

The transfer rates of gas molecules across liquid surfaces are profoundly affected by quite small quantities of surface active agents (present through both natural and human activities) and which are now known to be spread through oceanic and inland water bodies. Proteinaceous and lipid surfactants from biological decay are fairly common. While many studies in the past were on evaporative loss of water and transfer of dissolved material into the gas phase by bubble formation, not a great deal is known of the reverse process. But some information is available on the exchange of gas molecules through monomolecular layers on water. The stability of proteinaceous layers depends on a number of factors such as wind turbulence, but not the least of these may be the breakdown under solar irradiation. Photo-detachment of reducing species from solutes in water is known for a number of naturally occurring substances and the reactions of such are familiar from other sources[54].

A pertinent final comment about pollution studies is that much attention has been given to the effects of excess materials on living systems. Perhaps pollutant interactions leading to deficiencies of essential substances are worthy of some study. The point made is that while much remains to be done, evaluation and application of data from seemingly disparate areas provides a secure base from which to continue.

The writer is indebted to the Staff Development Committee of the WA Institute of Technology and the Natural Environmental Research Council of the UK for financial support.

References

1. Haagen-Smit, A. J. (1952). *Ind. Eng. Chem.* **44**, 1342.
2. Blacet, F. E. (1952). *Ind. Eng. Chem.* **44**, 1339.
3. Leighton, P. A. (1961). *Photochemistry of air pollution.* Academic Press, New York & London.
4. Norrish, R. & Oldershaw, G. (1959). *Proc. R. Soc.* **A249**, 498.
5. Dainton, F. S. & Ivin, K. J. (1950). *Trans. Far. Soc.* **46**, 374, 382.
6. Gerhard, E. R. & Johnstone, H. F. (1955). *Ind. Eng. Chem.* **47**, 972.
7. Renzetti, N. A. & Doyle, G. F. (1960). *Int. J. Air. Poll.* **2**, 327.
8. Okuda, S., Rao, T. N., Slater, D. H. & Calvert, J. G. (1969). *J. Phys. Chem.* **73**, 4412.
9. Urone, P., Lutsep, H., Noyes, C. M. & Parcher, J. F. (1968). *Env. Sci. Tech.* **2**, 611.
10. Cadle, R. D. & Allen, E. R. (1970). *Science* **167**, 243.
11. Sethi, D. S. (1971). *J. Air Poll. Control Ass.* **21**, 418.
12. Cox, R. A. (1972). *J. Phys. Chem.* **76**, 814.
13. Jacob, A. & Winkler, C. A. (1972). *J. Chem. Soc.* (Faraday) **68**, 2077.
14. Arin, L. M. & Warneck, P. (1972). *J. Phys. Chem.* **76**, 1514.
15. Johnston, H., Chang, S. & Whitten, G. (1974). *J. Phys. Chem.* **78**, 1.
16. Ghormley, J. A., Ellsworth, R. C. & Hochanadel, C. J. (1973). *J. Phys. Chem.* **77**, 1341.
17. Norrish, R. G. (1958). *Proc. Chem. Soc.* 247.
18. McGrath, W. D. & Norrish, R. G. (1958). *Nature, Lond.* **182**, 235.
19. Simonaitis, R. & Heicklen, J. (1973). *J. Phys. Chem.* **77**, 1096.
20. Bedford, G. & Thomas, J. H. (1972). *J. Chem. Soc.* (Faraday) **68**, 2163.
21. Elias, L. & Schiff, H. I. (1960). *Can. J. Chem.* **38**, 1657.
22. Bufalini, J. J., Gay, B. W. & Kopczynski, S. L. (1971). *Env. Sci. Tech.* **5**, 333.
23. Lin, C. L. & De More, W. B. (1973). *J. Phys. Chem.* **77**, 863.
24. Huie, R., Herron, J. T. & Davis, D. (1971). *J. Phys. Chem.* **75**, 3902.
25. Kurylo, M. J. & Huie, R. E. (1973). *J. Chem. Phys.* **58**, 1258.
26. Koda, S. (1974). *Can. J. Chem.* **52**, 287.
27. Glasson, W. A. & Tuesday, C. S. (1970). *Env. Sci. Tech.* **4**, 752.
28. Glasson, W. A. & Tuesday, C. S. (1970). *Env. Sci. Tech.* **4**, 916.
29. Chao, S. C. & Jaffe, S. (1972). *J. Chem. Phys.* **56**, 1987.
30. Gitchell, A., Simonaitis, R. & Heicklen, J. (1974). *J. Air Poll. Control Ass.* **24**, 357.
31. Altshuller, A. P. & Bufalini, J. J. (1965). *Photochem. Photobiol.* **4**, 97.
32. Hanst, P. L. (1971). *J. Air Poll. Control Ass.* **21**, 269.
33. Glasson, W. A. & Tuesday, C. S. (1970). *Env. Sci. Tech.* **4**, 37.
34. Altshuller, A. P., Kopczynski, S. L., Lonneman, W. A., Sutterfield, F. D. & Wilson, D. L. (1970). *Env. Sci. Tech.* **4**, 44.
35. Baulch, D. L., Drysdale, D. D., Horne, D. G. & Lloyd, A. C. (1972). *Evaluated kinetic data for high temperature reactions.* (Vol. 1 and subsequent vols.) Butterworth, London.
36. Donovan, R. J., Husain, D. & Kirsch, L. J. (1972). *Ann. Rep. Chem. Soc.* **69**, 19.
37. Johnstone, H. F. & Coughanowr (1958). *Ind. Eng. Chem.* **50**, 1169.
38. Cheng, R. T., Corn, M. & Frohliger, J. O. (1971). *Atmos. Env.* **5**, 987.
39. Bassett, H. & Parker, W. G. (1951). *J. Chem. Soc.* (Faraday) **68**, 1540.

40. McKay, H. A. C. (1971). *Atmos. Env.* **5**, 7.
41. Eggleton, A. E. J. & Atkins, D. H. (1972). *UKAEA Report R-6983.* HMSO, London.
42. Spedding, D. J. (1974). *Air pollution.* Oxford University Press, London.
43. Endow, N., Doyle, G. J. & Jones, J. L. (1963). *J. Air Poll. Control Ass.* **13**, 141.
44. Bergstrom, R. (1972). *Atmos. Env.* **6**, 247.
45. Wilson, W. E. & Levy, A. (1970). *J. Air Poll. Control Ass.* **20**, 385.
46. Cox, R. A. & Penkett, S. A. (1972). *J. Chem. Soc.* (Faraday) **68**, 1735.
47. Cox, R. A. (1974). *Tellus* **26**, 235.
48. Penkett, S. A. & Garland, J. A. (1974). *Tellus* **26**, 284.
49. Penkett, S. A. (1972). *Nature, Lond.* **240**, 105.
50. Wong, E. L. & Potter, A. E. (1965). *J. Chem. Phys.* **43**, 3371.
51. Crutzen, P. (1974). *Tellus* **26**, 47.
52. Miyamoto, S., Prather, R. J. & Bohn, H. L. (1974). *Proc. Soil Sci. Soc. Am.* **38**, 71.
53. Garland, J. A., Clough, W. S. & Fowler, D. (1973). *Nature, Lond.* **242**, 256.
54. *Radiation Research Reviews 1968–1969 Volume 1; Ann. Reports Chem. Soc.*

D.C.HORSMAN & A.R.WELLBURN

Appendix II. Guide to the metabolic and biochemical effects of air pollutants on higher plants

The following tables describe in abbreviated form most of the important metabolic and enzymic changes that take place when plants are exposed to ozone, peroxyacetylnitrate, ammonia, fluoride, sulphur dioxide, nitrogen dioxide and carbon monoxide; we have included, where appropriate, the effects of their known products in plant tissues. In each case the reader should consult the original paper to verify other environmental factors such as temperature, humidity and the age and nutrition of the plants studied. At present there appears to be no relevant literature on the effects of hydrogen sulphide, hydrogen chloride, nitric oxide or other possible atmospheric pollutants. The best guide to the atmospheric range of gaseous pollutants, both long-term and as transients, with the exception of sulphur dioxide, is provided by Saunders (1976) and the most informative review of metabolic effects is that of Ziegler (1973a).

It is the intention to revise and bring these tables up to date periodically and the senior author (ARW) would therefore appreciate relevant comments and information.

D. C. Horsman is grateful to the Natural Environment Research Council for financial support.

Table 1. *Reported metabolic or enzymic effects of peroxyacetylnitrate (PAN) on plants (excluding effects upon net photosynthesis, growth rate, crop yield or visible damage)*

Genus	Experimental conditions	Enzymatic or metabolic function	Effect	Reference*
Spinacia	Gassed chloroplast suspensions	Incorporation of acetate into fatty acids	Inhibited	75
Phaseolus	0.6–1 ppm for 0.5 h in the light	Photophosphorylation	Inhibited	29, 27
	0.6–1 ppm for 0.5 h in the light	NADP reduction	Inhibited	29, 27
	0.6–1 ppm for 0.5 h in the light	CO_2 fixation	Inhibited	29, 27
	0.6–1 ppm for 0.5 h in the dark	CO_2 fixation	Unaffected	29, 27
	0.6–1 ppm for 0.5 h in the light or dark	Photophosphorylation	Inhibited	55, 56
	1 ppm for 30 min	Sulphydryl level	Reduced	31
Avena	2.4 ppm for 6 h	Cellulose synthesis and metabolism	Inhibited	83
	Gassed enzyme solutions	NADPH-dependent isocitric dehydrogenase	Inactivated	77
	Gassed enzyme solutions	Glucose-6-phosphate dehydrogenase	Inactivated	77
	Gassed enzyme solutions	Malate dehydrogenase	Inactivated	77
	19–23 ppm for 6 h	Phosphoglucomutase	Inhibited	84
	19–23 ppm for 6 h	UDP- or GDP-glucose-dependent cell wall polysaccharide synthetase	Inhibited	85
	12–14 ppm for 4 h	UDP- or GDP-glucose-dependent cell wall polysaccharide synthetase	Inhibited	37

* See numbered reference list at end of Appendix for details.

Table 2. *Reported metabolic or enzymic effects of ozone (O_3) on plants (excluding effects upon net photosynthesis, growth rate, crop yield or visible damage)*

Genus	Experimental conditions	Enzymic or metabolic function	Effect	Reference*
Phaseolus	0.35 ppm for 20–35 min	Polysome number	Decreased	19
	0.23 ppm for 20–50 min	Number of SH-groups on chloroplast ribosomes	Reduced	20
	0.23 ppm for 20–50 min	23S chloroplast RNA level	Decreased	21
	0.15 ppm for 2 h	RNA level	Decreased	23
Avena	90–140 ppm for 6 h	Glucan and cellulose synthesis	Inhibited	86
Phaseolus	0.7–1 ppm for 30 min	Starch level	Decreased†	30
	0.7–1 ppm for 30 min	Sucrose and reducing sugars	Increased†	30
Citrus	0.25 ppm, 8 h/day, 5 d/week for 9 weeks	Reducing sugar level	Increased	26
	0.25 ppm 8 h/day, 5 d/week for 9 weeks	Uptake of [U-^{14}C] glucose	Increased	26
Pinus	0.15–0.45 ppm for 30 d	Polysaccharide level	Decreased	74
	0.15–0.45 ppm for 30 d	Soluble sugar level	Increased†	74
Cucumis and Cassia	0.05 ppm for 2–6 h	Starch hydrolysis in the dark	Decreased	42
Phaseolus and Mimulus	0.05 ppm for 2–6 h	Starch hydrolysis in the dark	Decreased	42
Petunia	0.04 ppm for 2.5 h	Ascorbic acid level	Decreased	43
Pinus	0.005–0.015 ppm for 35–154 d	Ascorbic acid level	Increased	12
	0.005–0.015 ppm for 35–154 d	Total soluble sugar level	Increased	12
Glycine	0.05 ppm for 2 h	Total soluble sugar level	Decreased	104
	0.05 ppm for 2 h	Reducing sugar level	Decreased	104
Citrus	0.15–0.25 ppm for 8 h over many days	Cell membrane permeability	Changed	28
Nicotiana	Gassed mitochondrial suspensions	Mitochondrial permeability	Increased	60
Pisum	Gassed chloroplast suspensions	Membrane permeability	Increased	82
Nicotiana	0.6–1.1 ppm for 1 h	Respiration	Stimulated	64
Phaseolus	0.25–0.3 ppm for 3 h	Respiration	Stimulated	91
Nicotiana	1 ppm for 1 h	Oxidative phosphorylation	Inhibited	58
Phaseolus, Spinacia and Nicotiana	1 ppm for 0.5–1 h	ATP levels	Decreased	106

Table 2 – *continued*

Genus	Experimental conditions	Enzymic or metabolic function	Effect	Reference*
Phaseolus	0.25–0.3 ppm for 3 h	ATP levels	Increased	91
Spinacia and *Brassica*	Gassed mitochondrial suspensions	Uptake of O_2 and citric acid cycle activity	Inhibited	35
Spinacia	0–0.41 ppm	Formation of formic acid	Increased	65
Nicotiana	1 ppm for 1 h	Saturated fatty acid levels	Decreased	107
	0.30 ppm for 2 h	Fatty acid levels	Unchanged	98
Phaseolus	0.025 ppm for 3 h	Sterol glucoside level	Increased	109
	0.025 ppm for 3 h	Esterified sterol glucoside level	Increased	109
	0.025 ppm for 3 h	Free sterol	Decreased	109
	0.025 ppm for 3 h	Monogalactosyl diglyceride	Decreased	109
Spinacia	Gassed chloroplast suspensions	Galactosyl diglyceride synthesis	Inhibited	76
Pinus	Not known	Methyl chavicol level in essential oil	Decreased	22
Rumex	Not known	Anthocyanin formation	Increased	54
Lemna	1 ppm for 4–24 h	Chlorophyll level	Decreased	32
Pinus	0.5 ppm for 9–18 d	Chlorophyll level	Decreased	73
Phaseolus	0.05–0.25 ppm for 2 h	Chlorophyll level	Decreased	23
Zea and *Glycine*	0.062–0.088 ppm for 4 h	Chlorophyll level	Decreased	61
Phaseolus	0.025 pphm for 3 h	Disulphide level	Increased	108
Gossypium	0.8 ppm for 1 h	Most free pool amino acid levels	Changed†	102
Phaseolus	1 ppm for 15 min	γ-amino-*n*-butyric acid levels	Increased	105
	1 ppm for 15 min	Alanine levels	Increased	105
	1 ppm for 15 min	Glutamic acid levels	Decreased	105
Glycine	0.05 ppm for 2 h	Nitrate reductase	Inhibited	103
	0.125–0.50 ppm for 2 h	NAD(P)H-dependent nitrate reductase	Inhibited	104
Zea and *Glycine*	0.062 ppm for 4 h	Nitrate reductase	Stimulated	61
	0.088 ppm for 4 h	Nitrate reductase	Inhibited	61
	0.062–0.088 ppm for 4 h	Nitrite reductase	Inhibited	61
Avena	125–250 ppm for 6 h	Phosphoglucomutase	Unchanged	84
	Gassed enzyme extracts	Phosphoglucomutase	Inhibited	84
Phaseolus	0.013–0.05 ppm for 30 min	Peroxidase	Stimulated	25
	0.02 ppm for 3 h	Peroxidase	Stimulated	24
	0.013–0.05 ppm for 30 min	Lactic dehydrogenase	Inhibited	25

Table 2 – *continued*

Genus	Experimental conditions	Enzymic or metabolic function	Effect	Reference*
Pinus	0.45 ppm for 12 h/day over 35 d	Acid phosphatase	Stimulated	33
Zea	0.062–0.088 ppm for 4 h	Alkaline pyrophosphatase	Inhibited	7
Phaseolus	0.015 ppm for 2 h	Ribonuclease	Stimulated	23
Nicotiana	0.6 ppm for 1 h	Cytochrome oxidase	Stimulated	64
	1.1 ppm for 1 h	Cytochrome oxidase	Inhibited	64

* See numbered reference list at end of Appendix for details.

† Leaf age dependency.

Table 3. *Reported metabolic or enzymic effects of carbon monoxide (CO) on plants (excluding effects upon net photosynthesis, growth rate, crop yield or visible damage)*

Genus	Experimental conditions	Enzymic or metabolic function	Effect	Reference*
N_2-fixing bacteria	Various	Nitrogen fixation	Inhibited	69
Chlorella	Gassed suspensions	O_2 evolution associated with NO_3^- reduction	Inhibited	110
	Gassed suspensions	Hill reaction	Inhibited	110
Phaseolus	200–360 ppm for 5–20 min	CO uptake and conversion to CO_2	Enhanced CO_2 fixation	14
Citrus	8 ppm for 5–20 min	CO_2 fixation	Strongly inhibited	14
Phoenix	5 ppm for 5–20 min	CO_2 fixation	Strongly inhibited	14

* See numbered reference list at end of Appendix for details.

Table 4. *Reported metabolic or enzymic effects of fluoride (both as HF and F^-) on plants (excluding effects upon net photosynthesis, growth rate, crop yield or visible damage)*

Genus	Experimental conditions	Enzymic or metabolic function	Effect	Reference*
Glycine and *Phaseolus*	1.3×10^{-2} M NaF	Chlorophyll synthesis	Inhibited	71
Zea	5×10^{-4}–5×10^{-3} M NaF	Ribosomes	Reduced in number	18
Lycopersicon	1.6 ppb for 8 d	Respiration	Increased	115
Phaseolus	1.6 ppb for 8 d	Respiration	Increased	115
	1.6 ppb for 8 d	Free sugar level	Increased	115
Lycopersicon	1.6 ppb for 8 d	Free sugar level	Increased	115
Phaseolus	1.7–7.6 μg m^{-3} for 10 d	Keto-acid levels	Decreased	70
	35×10^{-3} M KF for 0.5–2.5 min	Hill reaction activity below pH 5.6	Decreased	9
Avena	5×10^{-3} M NaF for 2 h	Cellulose synthesis	Inhibited	37
Chenopodium and *Polygonum*	0.006 ppm for 5–6 d	Pentose phosphate pathway	Stimulated	93
Glycine	0.03 ppm HF for 3–5 d	UDP-glucose-fructose transglucosylase	Inhibited	116, 117
	0.03 ppm HF for 3–5 d	PEP carboxylase	Stimulated	118
	0.03 ppm HF for 3–5 d	Phosphoglucomutase	Inhibited	116, 117
Avena	10^{-2} M NaF for 1 h	Phosphoglucomutase	Inhibited	84
Pisum	10^{-4}–10^{-2} M NaF	Enolase	Inhibited	72
Phaseolus	1.7–7.6 μg m^{-3} for 10 d	Enolase	Stimulated	70
Glycine	0.1 ppm for 24–144 h	Enolase	Stimulated	59
Sorghum	5 μg m^{-3} for 11 d	Enolase	Stimulated	70
	5 μg m^{-3} for 11 d	Catalase	Initially stimulated, later inhibited	70
Phaseolus	1.7–7.6 μg m^{-3} for 10 d	Catalase	Stimulated	70
Glycine	0.1 ppb for 24–144 h	Catalase	Stimulated	59
Sorghum	5 μg m^{-3} for 10 d	Pyruvate kinase	Stimulated	70
Pisum	5×10^{-4}–5×10^{-3} M NaF	Glucose-6-phosphate dehydrogenase	Stimulated	3
Glycine	0.1 ppb for 24–144 h	Glucose-6-phosphate dehydrogenase	Stimulated	59
	0.1 ppb for 24–144 h	Cytochrome oxidase	Stimulated	59
	0.1 ppb for 24–144 h	Polyphenol oxidase	Inhibited	59
	0.1 ppb for 24–144 h	Ascorbic acid oxidase	Initially stimulated, later inhibited	59
	0.1 ppb for 24–144 h	Peroxidase	Stimulated	59

* See numbered reference list at end of Appendix for details.

Table 5.   *Reported metabolic or enzymic effects of ammonia* (NH_3 *or* $NH_4{}^+$) *on plants* (*excluding effects upon net photosynthesis, growth rate, crop yield or visible damage*)

Genus	Experimental conditions	Enzymatic or metabolic function	Effect	Reference*
Zea	1–21 ppm for 24 h	Foliar uptake of ammonia into amides, amino acids and proteins	Indicated	92
Glycine, Zea, Gossypium and *Helianthus*	29–44 μg m^{-3} for 4–8 h/day or continuously	Mechanism of foliar uptake	Active and diurnal	46
Spinacia	2×10^{-4}–4.7×10^{-3} M on plastid suspension	Photosynthetic phosphorylation	Uncoupled	57
Pisum	1.2×10^{-4} M on reconstituted plastid suspension	PGA-stimulated oxygen evolution	Increased	96
Daucus	5×10^{-3} M for 2–20 d	Glycolysis	Stimulated	13
Hordeum	1.6×10^{-3} M	Respiration	Inhibited	111
Beta	Not indicated	NADH oxidation	Inhibited	114
	Ammonium treatment of mitochondrial suspension	NADH oxidation	Inhibited	111
Cucumis	Cultured with 20–200 mg l^{-1}	Ratios of NAD/NAD + NADH and NADP/NADP + NADPH	Little altered	113
	Cultured with 20 mg l^{-1}	Free sugar level	Decreased	66
	Cultured with 200 mg l^{-1}	Glucose level	Increased	66
	Cultured with 200 mg l^{-1}	Starch level	Decreased	66
	Cultured with 20–200 mg l^{-1}	UDP-glucose level	Increased	67
	Cultured with 20–200 mg l^{-1}	Starch granule and glucan synthesis	Inhibited	68
	Cultured with 20–200 mg l^{-1}	Glucose-6-phosphate dehydrogenase	Stimulated	112
	Cultured with 20–200 mg l^{-1}	Phosphogluco-isomerase	Stimulated	112
	Cultured with 20–200 mg l^{-1}	Phosphofructokinase	Stimulated	112
	Cultured with 20–200 mg l^{-1}	Glyceraldehyde-3-phosphate dehydrogenase	Stimulated	112
	Cultured with 20–200 mg l^{-1}	Enolase	Stimulated	112
	Cultured with 20–200 mg l^{-1}	Aconitase	Stimulated	112
	Cultured with 20–200 mg l^{-1}	NADP-dependent isocitric dehydrogenase	Stimulated	112
	Cultured with 20–200 mg l^{-1}	Peroxidase	Stimulated	112
	Cultured with 20–200 mg l^{-1}	Phosphofructokinase	Stimulated	112
	Cultured with 20–200 mg l^{-1}	Aldolase	Inhibited	112
	Cultured with 20–200 mg l^{-1}	Succinate dehydrogenase	Stimulated	69
	Cultured with 20–200 mg l^{-1}	Cytochrome *c* oxidase	Stimulated	69

Table 5 – *continued*

Genus	Experimental conditions	Enzymatic or metabolic function	Effect	Reference*
	Cultured with 20–200 mg l^{-1}	NADH-diaphorase	Stimulated	69
	Cultured with 20–200 mg l^{-1}	NADH-oxidase	Stimulated	69
	Cultured with 20–200 mg l^{-1}	Succinate: cytochrome c oxidoreductase	Stimulated	69
	Cultured with 20–200 mg l^{-1}	NADH: cytochrome c oxidoreductase	Stimulated	69
	Cultured with 20–200 mg l^{-1}	Mitochondrial ATPase	Stimulated	69
	Cultured with 20–200 mg l^{-1}	Glutamate dehydrogenase	Stimulated	112
Avena	15×10^{-3} M for 96 h	Glutamate dehydrogenase	Stimulated	11
	15×10^{-3} M for 96 h	Isocitric dehydrogenase	Stimulated	11
	15×10^{-3} M for 96 h	Malate dehydrogenase	Stimulated	11

* See numbered reference list at end of Appendix for details.

Table 6. *Reported metabolic or enzymic effects of sulphur dioxide (SO_2) and possible products (SO_3^{2-}, SO_4^{2-}, glyoxal bisulphite, etc.) on plants (excluding effects upon net photosynthesis, growth rate, crop yield or visible damage)*

Genus	Experimental conditions	Enzymic or metabolic process	Effect	Reference*
Vicia	1.5 ppm for 3.5 h	ATP levels	Increased	34
Nicotiana	0.3 ppm for 596 h	ATP levels	Increased	34
	1.7 ppm for 26 h	ATP levels	Decreased	34
Borago	1.3 ppm for 2 h	ATP levels	Decreased	34
Spinacia	5×10^{-3} M SO_3^{2-} on chloroplast suspensions	ATP levels	Decreased	62
Phaseolus and *Zea*	10^{-1} M SO_3^{2-} on mitochondrial suspensions	ATP levels	Decreased	10
Spinacia, Zea and *Amaranthus*	5×10^{-3} M glyoxal bisulphite	ATP levels	Decreased	63
Hordeum, Triticum and *Nicotiana*	10^{-2} M HSO_3^-	$^{14}CO_2$ fixation	Decreased	4
	10^{-2} M glyoxal bisulphite	$^{14}CO_2$ fixation	Decreased	4
	10^{-2} M glyoxylate bisulphite	$^{14}CO_2$ fixation	Decreased	4

Table 6 – *continued*

Genus	Experimental conditions	Enzymic or metabolic process	Effect	Reference*
Spinacia	5×10^{-3} M glyoxal bisulphite	$^{14}CO_2$ fixation	Decreased	5
	5×10^{-3} M SO_3^{2-} on chloroplast suspensions	$^{14}CO_2$ fixation	Decreased	5
Atriplex	10 mM HSO_3^-	$^{14}CO_2$ fixation	Decreased	87
	10 mM glyoxal bisulphite	$^{14}CO_2$ fixation	Decreased	87
Atriplex, *Spinacia* and *Zea*	5×10^{-4} M HSO_3^-	$^{14}CO_2$ fixation	Decreased	63
	5×10^{-4} M glyoxal bisulphite	$^{14}CO_2$ fixation	Decreased	63
Spinacia	1–5 mM SO_3^{2-}	$^{14}CO_2$ fixation	Decreased	62
	0–1 mM SO_3^{2-} on chloroplast suspensions	$^{14}CO_2$ fixation	Increased	62
	10^{-2} M SO_4^{2-} on chloroplast suspensions	Cyclic photophosphorylation	Decreased	6
	10^{-2} M SO_4^{2-} on chloroplast suspensions	Non-cyclic photophosphorylation	Decreased	6
	10^{-2} M SO_4^{2-} on chloroplast suspensions	Non-cyclic and cyclic photophosphorylation	Decreased	94
	10^{-2}–2×10^{-2} M SO_4^{2-} on chloroplast suspensions	HCO_3^--stimulated O_2 evolution	Decreased	8
	10^{-2}–2×10^{-2} M SO_4^{2-} on chloroplast suspensions	PGA-stimulated O_2 evolution	Decreased	8
Acer	125 ppm for 17 h	Pentose phosphate cycle activity	Increased	81
Betula	125 ppm for 17 h	Pentose phosphate cycle activity	Decreased	81
Acer	125 ppm for 17 h	Glycolysis and citric acid cycle activity	Decreased	81
Betula	125 ppm for 17 h	Glycolysis and citric acid cycle activity	Increased	81
Pisum	10 000 ppm for 24–96 h	Keto-acid levels	Decreased	50
Hordeum	5 ppm for 0.25–1 h	Glycolate formation	Increased	95
	5 ppm for 0.25–1 h	Sugar phosphate formation	Increased	95
	5 ppm for 0.25–1 h	Sucrose formation	Decreased	95
Picea	(Atmospheric)	Sugar levels	Increased	15
Pisum	10 000 ppm for 24–96 h	Sucrose level	Decreased	53
	10 000 ppm for 24–96 h	Glucose and fructose levels	Increased	53
	10 000 ppm for 24–96 h	Alanine level	Increased	53
	10 000 ppm for 24–96 h	Glutamate level	Decreased	53

Table 6 – *continued*

Genus	Experimental conditions	Enzymic or metabolic process	Effect	Reference*
Lolium, Phaseolus and *Trifolium*	0.25 ppm for 14 d	Free amino acid levels	Changed, generally increased	1
Phaseolus	0.7 ppm up to 3 d	Free amino acid levels	Changed, generally increased	36
	0.7 ppm up to 3 d	Aspartate and glutamate levels	Decreased	36
Pisum	0.3–1.3 ppm for 7–21 d	Glutamate levels	Initially increased, later decreased	47, 48
	0.3–1.3 ppm for 7–21 d	Glutamine levels	Increased	47, 48
	0.3–1.3 ppm for 7–21 d	Cysteine levels	Increased	48
	0.3–1.3 ppm for 7–21 d	Inorganic and organic sulphur levels	Increased	48
Picea	1.4–2.2 ppm (length not given)	Inorganic and organic sulphur levels	Increased	49
	(Atmospheric)	Water soluble sulphydryl levels	Increased	40, 41
Oryza	10 ppm for 70 h	Formation of glyoxylate bisulphite	Detected	99
Pisum	10 000 ppm for 24–96 h	Formation of α hydroxysulphonates	Detected	50
Brassica	3.4 ppm for 3.5 h	Vitamin B levels	Decreased	34
Abies	0.5 ppm (length not given)	Chlorophyll *a/b* ratio	Decreased	79
Avena, Hordeum and *Secale*	0.13 ppm (length not given)	Chlorophylls *a* and *b*, and β-carotene levels	Decreased	2, 44
Hordeum	5 ppm for 0.25–1 h	Pigment formation	Decreased	95
Alfalfa	Not given fully	Diastase	Stimulated	101
	Not given fully	Catalase	Inhibited	101
Acer and *Betula*	Not given fully	Catalase	Inhibited	80
	Not given fully	Peroxidase	Generally stimulated	80
	Not given fully	Polyphenol oxidase	Generally stimulated	80
Pisum	0.2–2 ppm for 6 d	Peroxidase	Stimulated	44
	0.3–1.3 ppm for 7–21 d	Glutamate dehydrogenase	Reductive amination stimulated	47, 90
	0.3–1.3 ppm for 7–21 d	Glutamate dehydrogenase	Oxidative deamination inhibited	90

Table 6 – *continued*

Genus	Experimental conditions	Enzymic or metabolic process	Effect	Reference*
	0.66×10^{-3} M Na_2S or Na_2SO_3	Glutamate dehydrogenase	Inhibited	90
	0.66×10^{-3} M $Na_2S_2O_3$ or $(NH_4)_2SO_4$	Glutamate dehydrogenase	Stimulated	90
	0.3 ppm for 10 d	Glutamate dehydrogenase	Isoenzyme pattern changed	90, 88
Nicotiana	0.3 ppm for 436 h	NADP-dependent glyceraldehyde-3-phosphate dehydrogenase	Stimulated	34
Vicia	0.3 ppm for 72 h	NADP-dependent glyceraldehyde-3-phosphate dehydrogenase	Stimulated	34
Nicotiana and *Vicia*	1.6 ppm for 5.5 h	NADP-dependent glyceraldehyde-3-phosphate dehydrogenase	Inhibited	34
Pisum	0.3 ppm for 7–21 d	Glutamine synthetase	Slightly stimulated	90
	Gaseous treatment not given	Glutamate oxaloacetate transaminase (mitochondrial)	Inhibited	89
	10^{-4}–3×10^{-4} M $SO_3{}^{2-}$	Glutamate oxaloacetate transaminase (mitochondrial)	Inhibited	89
	10 000 ppm for 48 h	Glutamate oxaloacetate transaminase	Inhibited	51
	0.2–2 ppm for 6 d	Glutamate pyruvate transaminase	Slightly stimulated	44
	10 000 ppm for 48 h	Aspartate pyruvate transaminase	Inhibited	51
Spinacia	2×10^{-2} M $SO_3{}^{2-}$ on chloroplast fragments	Ribulose-1,5-diphosphate carboxylase	Inactivated	120
Pisum	0.2–2 ppm for 6 d	Ribulose-1,5-diphosphate carboxylase	Inhibited	44
Atriplex	10^{-3} M glyoxal bisulphite	Malate dehydrogenase	Inhibited	87
Spinacia and *Zea*	5×10^{-3} M $SO_3{}^{2-}$	Malate dehydrogenase	Inactivated	122
Atriplex	10^{-3} M glyoxal bisulphite	Phosphoenolpyruvate carboxylase	Inhibited	87
Zea	10^{-2} M $SO_3{}^{2-}$	Phosphoenolpyruvate carboxylase	Inactivated	122
Spinacia	10^{-2} M $SO_3{}^{2-}$ (also bisulphite cpds)	Phosphoenolpyruvate carboxylase	Inactivated (also with bisulphite cpds)	78

Table 6 – *continued*

Genus	Experimental conditions	Enzymic or metabolic process	Effect	Reference*
Atriplex, *Spinacia* and *Zea*	5×10^{-3} M glyoxal bisulphite	Phosphoenolpyruvate carboxylase	Inhibited	63
	5×10^{-3} M glyoxal bisulphite	Glycolate oxidase	Inhibited	63

* See numbered reference list at end of Appendix for details.

Table 7.   *Reported metabolic or enzymic effects of nitrogen dioxide (NO_2 and NO_2^-) on plants (excluding effects upon net photosynthesis, growth rate, crop yield or visible damage)*

Genus	Experimental conditions	Metabolic or enzymic process	Effect	Reference*
Lycopersicon and *Phaseolus*	0.15–0.5 ppm for 10–22 days	Nitrate nitrogen level	Decreased	100
Hordeum	10 mM NO_2^-	Incorporation of $^{15}NO_3^-$	Inhibited	17
(Not stated)	Not known	β-carotene level	Decreased	52
	Not known	Chlorophyll level	(Phaeophytin formed)	52
Lycopersicon and *Phaseolus*	0.15–0.5 ppm for 10–22 d	Chlorophyll level	Increased	100
Pisum	0.1–1 ppm for 6 d	Chlorophyll level	Increased	44
Spinacia	0.1–0.5 mM NO_2^- on chloroplast suspensions	HCO_3^--dependent O_2 evolution	Decreased	38
	1 mM NO_2^- on chloroplast suspensions	NADP-dependent evolution	Decreased	38
	0.1–10 mM NO_2^- on chloroplast suspensions	NADP-dependent O_2 evolution	Not affected	39
	0.1 mM NO_2^- on chloroplast suspensions	NADPH levels	Increased	39
Pisum and *Phaseolus*	4–12 ppm for up to 1 h	Nitrate reductase	Stimulated	119
Pisum	0.1–1 ppm for 6 d	Ribulose-1,5-diphosphate carboxylase	Stimulated	44
	0.1–1 ppm for 6 d	Glutamate oxaloacetate transaminase	Unaffected	44
	0.1–1 ppm for 6 d	Glutamate pyruvate transaminase	Unaffected	44
	0.1–1 ppm for 6 d	Peroxidase	Unaffected	44

* See numbered reference list at end of Appendix for details.

References

1. Arndt, U. (1970). *Staub-Reinhalt.* **30**, 256–9.
2. Arndt, U. (1971). *Environ. Pollut.* **2**, 37–48.
3. Arrigoni, O. & Marré, E. (1955). *G. Biochim.* **4**, 1–9.
4. Asada, K. & Kasai, Z. (1962). *Plant Cell Physiol.* **3**, 125–36.
5. Asada, K., Kitoh, S., Deura, R. & Kasai, Z. (1965). *Plant Cell Physiol.* **6**, 615–29.
6. Asada, K., Deura, R. & Kasai, Z. (1968). *Plant Cell Physiol.* **9**, 143–6.
7. Baggett, L. B., Leffler, H. R. & Cherry, J. H. (1973). *Plant Physiol. (Suppl.)* **51**, 112.
8. Baldry, C. W., Cockburn, W. & Walker, D. A. (1968). *Biochim. Biophys. Acta* **153**, 476–83.
9. Ballantyne, D. J. (1972). *Atmos. Environ.* **6**, 267–73.
10. Ballantyne, D. J. (1973). *Phytochem.* **12**, 1207–9.
11. Barash, I., Sadan, T. & Mor, H. (1974). *Plant Cell Physiol.* **15**, 563–6.
12. Barnes, R. L. (1972). *Can. J. Bot.* **50**, 215–19.
13. Beccari, E., Dagnold, G., Morpurgo, G. & Pocchiari, F. (1969). *J. Exp. Bot.* **20**, 110–12.
14. Bidwell, R. R. S. & Fraser, D. E. (1972). *Can. J. Bot.* **50**, 1435–9.
15. Börtitz, S. (1969). *Arch. Fortswes.* **18**, 123–31.
16. Burris, R. H. (1969). *Ann. Rev. Plant Physiol.* **17**, 155–79.
17. Canvin, D. T. & Atkins, C. A. (1974). *Planta* **116**, 207–24.
18. Chang, Ch.W. (1970). *Physiol. Plant.* **23**, 536–43.
19. Chang. Ch.W. (1971a). *Phytochem.* **10**, 2863–8.
20. Chang, Ch.W. (1971b). *Biochem. Biophys. Res. Commun.* **44**, 1429–35.
21. Chang, Ch.W. (1972). *Phytochem.* **11**, 1347–50.
22. Cobb, F. W., Zavarine, E. & Bergot, J. (1972). *Phytochem.* **11**, 1815–18.
23. Craker, L. E. & Starbuck, J. S. (1972). *Can. J. Pl. Sci.* **52**, 589–97.
24. Curtis, C. R. & Howell, R. K. (1971). *Phytopath.* **61**, 1306–7.
25. Dass, H. S. & Weaver, G. M. (1968). *Can. J. Pl. Sci.* **48**, 569–74.
26. Dugger, W. M., Koukol, J. & Palmer, R. L. (1966). *J. Air Pollut. Control Assoc.* **16**, 467–71.
27. Dugger, W. M., Mudd, J. B. & Koukol, J. (1965). *Arch. Environ. Health* **10**, 195–200.
28. Dugger, W. M., Koukol, J. & Palmer, R. L. (1965). *Plant Physiol. (Suppl.)* **40**, xx.
29. Dugger, W. M., Koukol, J., Reed, W. D. & Palmer, R. L. (1963). *Plant Physiol.* **38**, 468–72.
30. Dugger, W. M., Taylor, O. C., Cardiff, E. & Thompson, C. R. (1962). *J. Am. Soc. Hort. Sci.* **81**, 304–15.
31. Dugger, W. M. & Ting, I. P. (1968). *Phytopath.* **58**, 1102–7.
32. Erickson, L. C. & Wedding, R. T. (1956). *Am. J. Bot.* **43**, 32–6.
33. Evans, L. S. & Miller, P. R. (1972). *Am. J. Bot.* **59**, 297–304.
34. Fischer, K. (1971). *Bundesversuchsanstalt (Vienna)* **92**, 209–31.
35. Freebairn, H. T. (1973). *Science* **126**, 303–4.
36. Godzik, S. & Linskens, H. F. (1974). *Environ. Pollut.* **7**, 25–38.
37. Gordon, W. C. & Ordin, L. (1972). *Plant Physiol.* **49**, 542–5.
38. Grant, B. R. & Canvin, D. T. (1970). *Planta* **95**, 227–46.
39. Grant, B. R., Labelle, R. & Mangat, B. S. (1972). *Planta* **106**, 181–4.

40. Grill, D. & Esterbauer, H. (1973a). *Phyton (Austria)* **15**, 87–101.

41. Grill, D. & Esterbauer, H. (1973b). *Eur. J. For. Path.* **3**, 65–71.

42. Hanson, G. P. & Stewart, W. S. (1970). *Science* **168**, 1223–4.

43. Hanson, G. P., Throne, L. & Jativa, C. P. (1970). *Lasca Leaves* **20**, 6–7.

44. Horsman, D. C. & Wellburn, A. R. (1975). *Environ. Pollut.* **8**, 123–33.

45. Howell, R. K. (1970). *Phytopath.* **60**, 1626–9.

46. Hutchinson, G. L., Millington, R. J. & Peters, D. B. (1972). *Science* **175**, 771–2.

47. Jäger, H. J. & Pahlich, E. (1972). *Oecologia* **9**, 135–40.

48. Jäger, H. J., Pahlich, E. & Steubing, L. (1972). *Angew. Bot.* **46**, 199–211.

49. Jäger, H. J. & Steubing, L. (1970). *Angew. Bot.* **44**, 209–21.

50. Jiráček, V., Macháčková, I. and Koštíř, J. (1972a). *Experientia* **28**, 1007–9.

51. Jiráček, V., Macháčková, I. and Koštíř, J. (1972b). *Experientia* **28**, 1164–5.

52. Kändler, U. & Ullrich, H. (1964). *Naturwissenschaften* **51**, 518.

53. Koštíř, J., Macháčková, I., Jiráček, V. & Buchar, E. (1970). *Experientia* **26**, 604–5.

54. Koukol, J. & Dugger, W. M. (1967). *Plant Physiol.* **42**, 1023–4.

55. Koukol, J., Dugger, W. M. & Belsner, N. O. (1963). *Plant Physiol. (Suppl.)* **38**, xii.

56. Koukol, J., Dugger, W. M. & Palmer, R. L. (1967). *Plant Physiol.* **42**, 1419–22.

57. Krogman, D. W., Jagendorf, A. T. & Avron, M. (1959). *Plant Physiol.* **34**, 272–7.

58. Lee, T. T. (1967). *Plant Physiol.* **42**, 691–6.

59. Lee, C-J., Miller, G. W. & Welkie, G. W. (1966). *Int. J. Air Water Pollut.* **10**, 169–81.

60. Lee, T. T. (1968). *Plant Physiol.* **43**, 133–9.

61. Leffler, H. R. & Cherry, J. H. (1974). *Can. J. Bot.* **52**, 1233–8.

62. Libera, W., Ziegler, H. & Ziegler, I. (1973). *Planta* **109**, 269–79.

63. Luttge, V., Osmond, C. B., Ball, E., Brinkmann, E. & Kinze, G. (1972). *Plant Cell Physiol.* **13**, 505–14.

64. Macdowall, F. D. H. (1965). *Can. J. Bot.* **43**, 419–27.

65. Mader, P. P., Cann, G. & Palmer, L. (1965). *Plant Physiol.* **30**, 318–23.

66. Matsumoto, H., Wakiuchi, N. & Takahashi, E. (1968). *Physiol. Plant.* **21**, 1210–16.

67. Matsumoto, H., Wakiuchi, N. & Takahashi, E. (1969). *Physiol. Plant.* **22**, 537–45.

68. Matsumoto, H., Wakiuchi, N. & Takahashi, E. (1971a). *Physiol. Plant.* **24**, 102–5.

69. Matsumoto, H., Wakiuchi, N. & Takahashi, E. (1971b). *Physiol. Plant.* **25**, 353–7.

70. McCune, D. C., Weinstein, L. H., Jacobson, J. S. & Hitchcock, A. E. (1964). *J. Air Pollut. Control Assoc.* **14**, 465–8.

71. McNulty, I. B. & Newman, D. W. (1961). *Plant Physiol.* **36**, 385–8.

72. Miller, G. W. (1958). *Plant Physiol.* **33**, 199–206.

73. Miller, P. R., Parmeter, J. R., Taylor, O. C. & Cardiff, E. A. (1963). *Phytopath.* **53**, 1072–6.

74. Miller, P. R., Parmeter, J. R., Flick, B. H. & Martinez, C. W. (1969). *J. Air. Pollut. Control Assoc.* **19**, 435–8.

75. Mudd, J. B. & Dugger, W. M. (1963). *Arch. Biochem. Biophys.* **102**, 52–8.

76. Mudd, J. B., McManus, T. T., Ongun, A. & McCullogh, T. E. (1971). *Plant Physiol.* **48**, 335–9.

77. Mudd, J. B. (1963). *Arch. Biochem. Biophys.* **102**, 59–65.

78. Mukerji, S. K. & Yang, S. F. (1974). *Plant Physiol.* **53**, 829–34.

79. Müller, J. (1957). *Naturwissenschaften* **44**, 453.

80. Nikolaevskiy, V. S. (1966). *Okrana Prirody na Urale* **5**, 19–23.

81. Nikolaevskiy, V. S. (1968). *Fiziol. Rast. (Moscow)* **15**, 110–15.

82. Nobel, P. S. & Wang, C-T. (1973). *Arch. Biochem. Biophys.* **157**, 388–94.
83. Ordin, L. (1962). *Plant Physiol.* **37**, 603–8.
84. Ordin, L. & Altmann, A. (1965). *Physiol. Plant.* **18**, 790–7.
85. Ordin, L. & Hall, M. A. (1967). *Plant Physiol.* **42**, 205–12.
86. Ordin, L. & Skoe, B. B. (1964). *Plant Physiol.* **39**, 751–5.
87. Osmond, C. B. & Avadhani, P. N. (1970). *Plant Physiol.* **45**, 228–30.
88. Pahlich, E. (1972). *Planta* **104**, 78–88.
89. Pahlich, E. (1973). *Planta* **110**, 267–78.
90. Pahlich, E., Jäger, H-J. & Steubing, L. (1972). *Angew. Bot.* **46**, 183–97.
91. Pell, E. J. & Brennan, E. (1973). *Plant Physiol.* **51**, 378–81.
92. Porter, L. K., Viets, F. G. & Hutchinson, G. L. (1972). *Science* **175**, 759–61.
93. Ross, C. W., Wicbe, H. H. & Miller, G. W. (1962). *Plant Physiol.* **37**, 305–9.
94. Ryrie, I. J. & Jagendorf, A. T. (1971). *J. Biol. Chem.* **246**, 582–8.
95. Spedding, D. J. & Thomas, W. J. (1973). *Aust. J. Biol. Sci.* **26**, 281–6.
96. Stokes, D. M. & Walker, D. A. (1971). *Plant Physiol.* **48**, 163–5.
97. Saunders, P. J. W. (1976). Inter-research Council Committee on Pollution Research, Seminar, May 1974. Appendix Table 1.
98. Swanson, E. S., Thomson, W. W. & Mudd, J. B. (1973). *Can. J. Bot.* **51**, 1213–19.
99. Tanaka, H., Takanashi, T. & Yatazawa, M. (1972). *Water, Air and Soil Pollut.* **1**, 205–11.
100. Taylor, O. C. & Eaton, F. M. (1966). *Plant Physiol.* **41**, 132–5.
101. Thomas, M. D., Hendricks, R. H. & Hill, G. R. (1950). *Ind. Eng. Chem.* **42**, 2231–5.
102. Ting, I. P. & Mukerji, S. K. (1971). *Am. J. Bot.* **58**, 497–504.
103. Tingey, D. T., Fites, R. C. & Wickliff, C. (1973a). *Physiol. Plant* **29**, 33–8.
104. Tingey, D. T., Fites, R. C. & Wickliff, C. (1973b). *Environ. Pollut.* **4**, 183–92.
105. Tomlinson, H. & Rich, S. (1967). *Phytopath.* **57**, 972–4.
106. Tomlinson, H. & Rich, S. (1968). *Phytopath.* **58**, 808–10.
107. Tomlinson, H. & Rich, S. (1969). *Phytopath.* **59**, 1284–6.
108. Tomlinson, H. & Rich, S. (1970). *Phytopath.* **60**, 1842–3.
109. Tomlinson, H. & Rich, S. (1971). *Phytopath.* **61**, 132.
110. Vennesland, B. & Jetschmann, C. (1971). *Arch. Biochem. Biophys.* **144**, 428–37.
111. Vines, H. M. & Wedding, R. T. (1960). *Plant Physiol.* **35**, 820–5.
112. Wakiuchi, N., Matsumoto, H. & Takahashi, E. (1971). *Physiol. Plant.* **24**, 248–53.
113. Wakiuchi, N., Matsumoto, H., Kondo, S. & Takahashi, E. (1972). *Physiol. Plant.* **26**, 230–2.
114. Wedding, R. T. & Vines, H. M. (1959). *Nature, Lond.* **184**, 1226–7.
115. Weinstein, L. H. (1961). *Contr. Boyce Thompson Inst.* **21**, 215–31.
116. Yang, S-F. & Miller, G. W. (1962). *Plant Physiol. (Suppl.)* **37**, I xix.
117. Yang, S-F. & Miller, G. W. (1963a). *Biochem. J.* **88**, 509–16.
118. Yang, S-F. & Miller, G. W. (1963b). *Biochem. J.* **88**, 517–22.
119. Zeevaart, A. J. (1974). *Acta Bot. Neerl.* **23**, 345–6.
120. Ziegler, I. (1972). *Planta* **103**, 155–63.
121. Ziegler, I. (1973a). *Environmental quality and safety*, vol. 2, Eds F. Coulston & F. Korte, pp. 182–208. Georg Thieme/Academic Press, New York.
122. Ziegler, I. (1973b). *Phytochem.* **12**, 1027–30.
123. Ziegler, I. (1974). *Phytochem.* **13**, 2411–16.

INDEX

Abies, sulphur dioxide effect on, 194
Acer, sulphur dioxide effects on, 193, 194
acetyl radical, in air chemistry, 169
acid phosphatase, in lead-tolerant and
  non-tolerant *Agrostis*, 124
Acrocephalus robertii, uptake of cobalt
  by, 118
acrylic plastic, for walls of plant
  chambers, 33–4
aerodynamic resistance, to transfer
  between atmosphere and leaf surface,
  9–10
aerosols, 164n, 176–7; mechanism of
  formation of, 178–80; oxidation of
  sulphur dioxide in, 174–6
Aesculus hippocastanum, zinc on leaves
  of, 116
Agrostis canina, copper- and zinc-tolerant
  strains of, 116
Agrostis stolonifera: copper-tolerant
  strains of, 116, 139, 143, 144, 147;
  variation of esterase isoenzymes in,
  143; zinc-tolerant strains of, 116
Agrostis tenuis: acid phosphatase in
  lead-tolerant and non-tolerant strains
  of, 124; copper-tolerant strains of, 116,
  141, 143, 147, 153; distribution of
  copper tolerance in population of, 150,
  151; distribution of copper-tolerant
  strains of, round copper mine, 154;
  fitness of metal-tolerant strains of, in
  normal conditions, 148, 149, 152;
  malate in leaves of metal-tolerant and
  non-tolerant strains of, 126; metals in
  cell walls of, 119, 120, 138–9; uptake
  of metals by, 117, 120; variability in
  copper tolerance in, 147; zinc-tolerant
  strains of, 116, 151–2
air distribution system (plenum), in open-
  top experimental chambers, 35–7

alfalfa: order of absorption of pollutant
  gases by, 17; sulphur dioxide effects
  on, 194; uptake and loss of fluoride by,
  19
algae in lichens: as percentage of thallus,
  63; potassium release from, on
  exposure to sulphur dioxide, 70;
  relative sensitivity of fungi and, to
  sulphur dioxide, 63; resynthesis of
  lichens from fungi and, 81
alkyl radicals, in air chemistry, 169, 171,
  172
aluminium smelters, fluoride from, 38
Amaranthus, glyoxal bisulphite effect on,
  192
amine radical, in air chemistry, 170, 180
ammonia
  in air chemistry, 167; interacts with
    hydroxyl radical, 181, and with
    nitrogen dioxide, 170; promotes
    oxidation of sulphur dioxide, 177;
  effects of, on enzymes, alone, 107, 109,
    191–2, and with sulphur dioxide,
    109; effects of, on plant metabolism,
    191; strains of *Ulva* resistant to, 136
Anthoxanthum odoratum: distribution
  of zinc-tolerant strains of, at boundary
  of zinc-containing soil, 151–2; fitness
  of metal-tolerant strains of, in normal
  conditions, 148, 149, 152; inheritance
  of zinc tolerance in, 138, 139; uptake
  of metals by, 117
Armeria maritima: uptake of metals by,
  117; zinc-tolerant strains of, require
  zinc in soil, 148
Arrhenatherum elatium, shows little
  variability in copper tolerance, 147–8
arsenic, uptake of, 118
Aspergillus niger, sulphydryl groups in
  mercury-tolerant strains of, 124